Viz Graphic Novel

FLAME OF RECCA

™

Vol. 5
Action Edition

Story and Art by
Nobuyuki Anzai

Flame of Recca
Vol. 5
Gollancz Manga Edition

Story and Art by
Nobuyuki Anzai

English Adaptation/Lance Caselman
Translation/Joe Yamazaki
Touch-Up & Lettering/Kelle Han
Graphics & Cover Design/Sean Lee
Editor/Eric Searleman
Uk Cover Adaptation/Sue Michniewicz

1 3 5 7 9 10 8 6 4 2

The right of Nobuyuki Anzai to be identified as the author of this work has been
asserted by him in accordance with the Copyright, Designs and Patents Act 1988.

A CIP catalogue record for this book is
available from the British Library

ISBN-13 978 0 57508 017 1
ISBN-10 0 57508 017 5

Printed and bound at Mackays of Chatham, PLC

The Orion Publishing Group's policy is to use papers that are natural, renewable
and recyclable products and made from wood grown in sustainable forests. The logging
and manufacturing processes are expected to conform to the environmental
regulations of the country of origin.

www.orionbooks.co.uk

Viz Graphic Novel

FLAME OF RECCA™

Vol. 5

Story & Art by Nobuyuki Anzai

Contents

Bonus Story
My Picture Diary: Kurogane (Iron) Kobushi
Tekken Version

PART FORTY:
YOU CALLED ME "MOTHER"

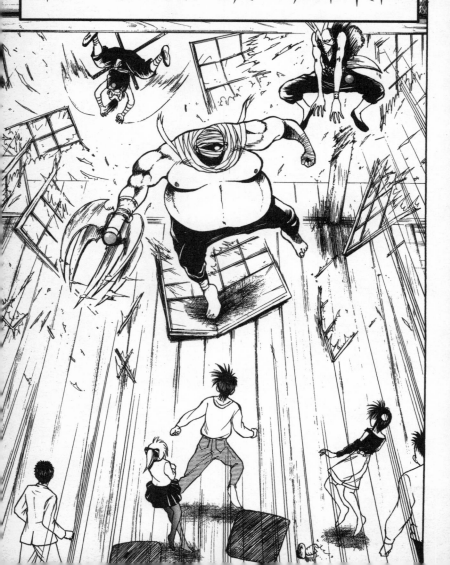

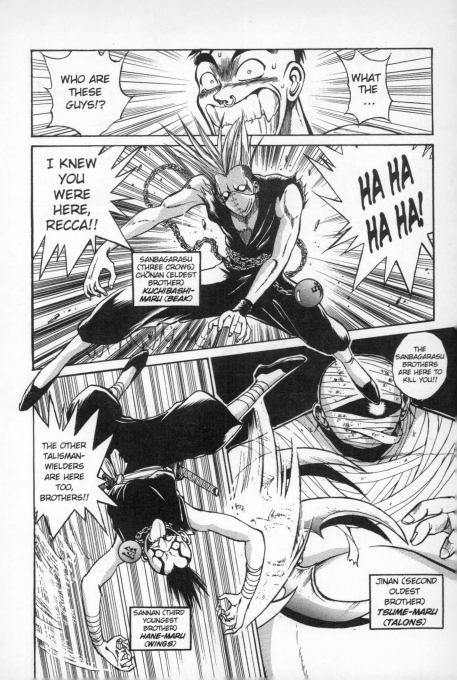

GASP

WHAT A TASTY-LOOKING DISH... HEH HEH.

HMM... AND THE GIRL OF HEALING.

HEY, THREE STOOGES!!

AND WE HATE BEING CALLED "STOOGES."

WE'RE THE SANBAGARASU BROTHERS, BRAT!!

LET'S TAKE THIS OUTSIDE!

KEEP YOUR DIRTY PAWS OFF MY PRINCESS!

YOU'RE DEAD, THAT'S WHAT.

WHAT IF WE ARE!!?

ARE YOU KUREI'S HENCHMEN?

KRAK KRAK

HE'S IN A BAD MOOD.

HE'S ALWAYS LIKE THAT, MISS SAKOSHITA.

RECCA SEEMS ANGRIER THAN USUAL.

UM...

HIS FEW BRAIN CELLS ARE STARTING TO SMOKE.

HE DOESN'T KNOW IF KAGERŌ WAS TELLING THE TRUTH ABOUT HIS ORIGINS.

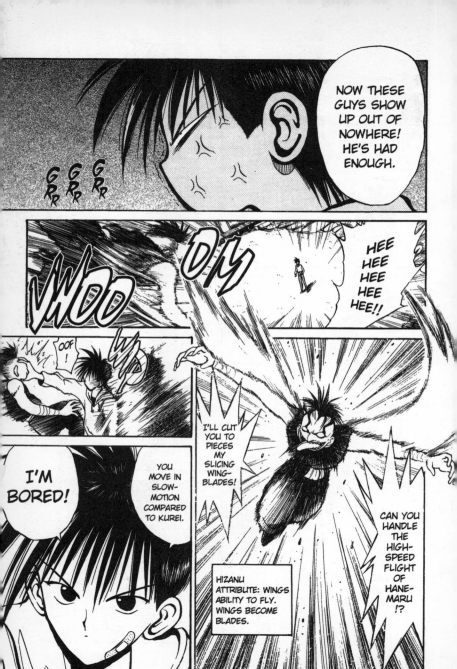

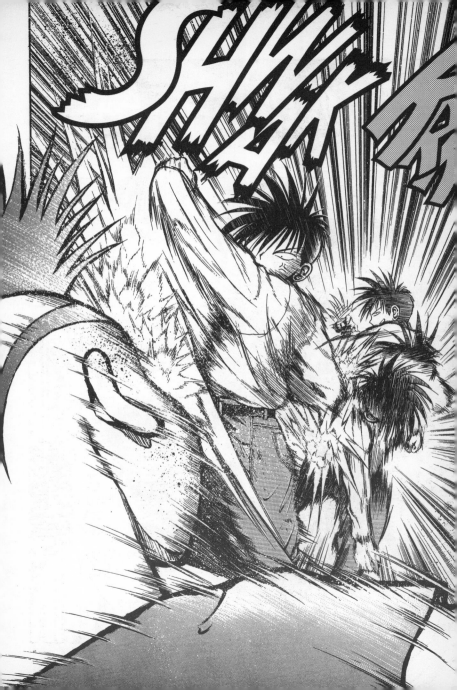

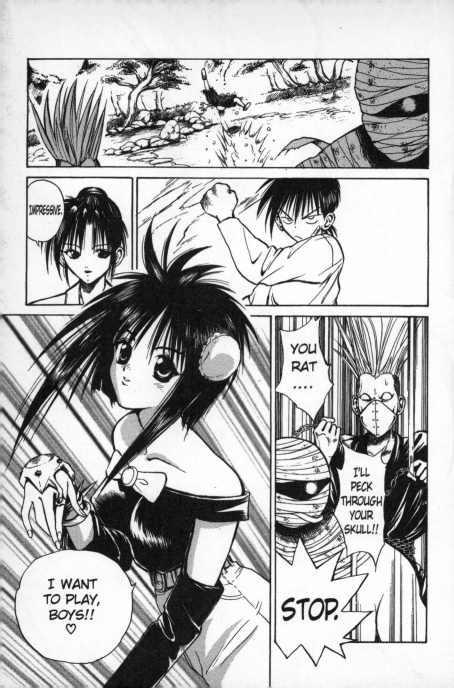

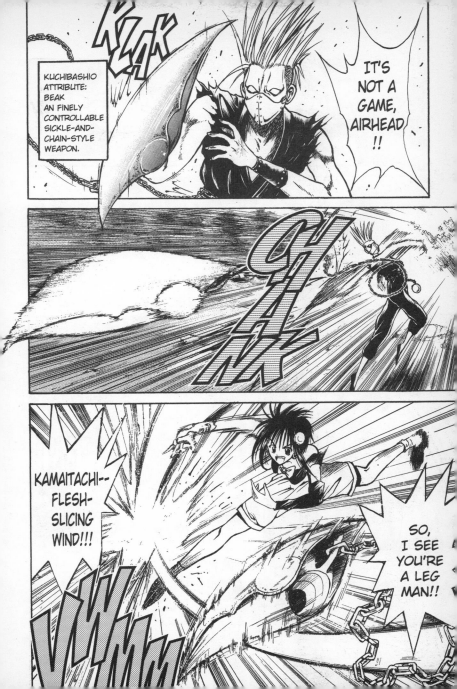

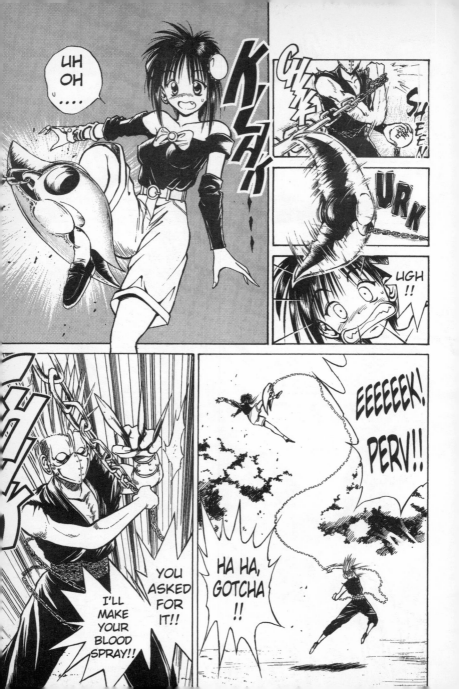

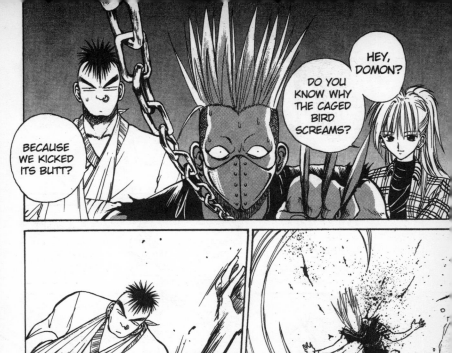

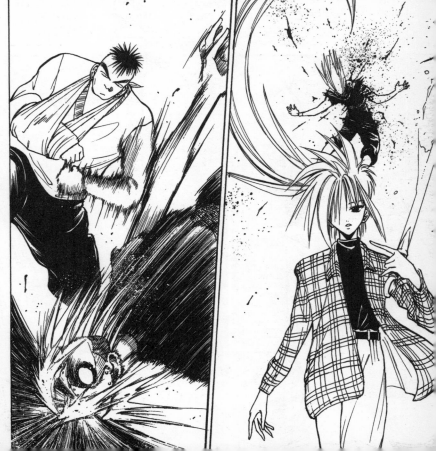

THEY UNDER-ESTIMATED YOU.

THEY ARE BECOMING ACCUSTOMED TO FIGHTING AGAINST TALISMANS AND WEAPONS.

IN THE HANDS OF ASSASSINS WHO KNOW HOW TO USE THEM.

THOSE WEAPONS CAN BE FORMIDABLE ...

THEY WERE GENIN-- SECOND-RATE NINJAS.

TSUME-MARU!! AT LEAST SLICE THE WEAKEST-LOOKING ONE TO PIECES!!

!#@%!

THESE AREN'T NORMAL KIDS!? THEY'RE PROS!!!

UGH

!?

ONI NO TSUME (THE DEVIL'S CLAWS) ATTRIBUTE: TALONS FIVE BLADES IN THE FORM OF TALONS, SHARPER EVEN THAN THE KŌGON ANKIN.

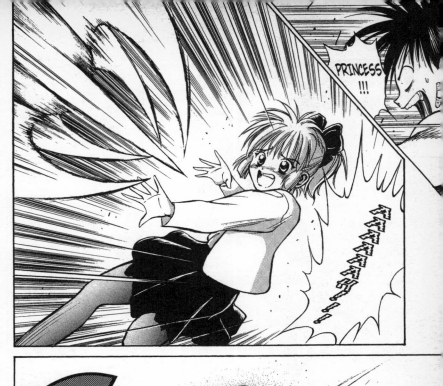
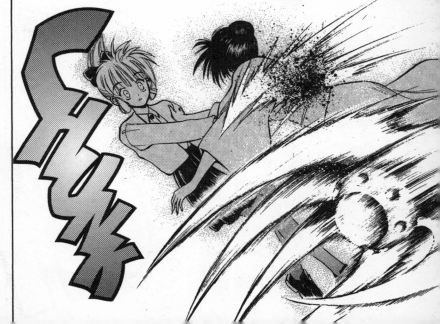

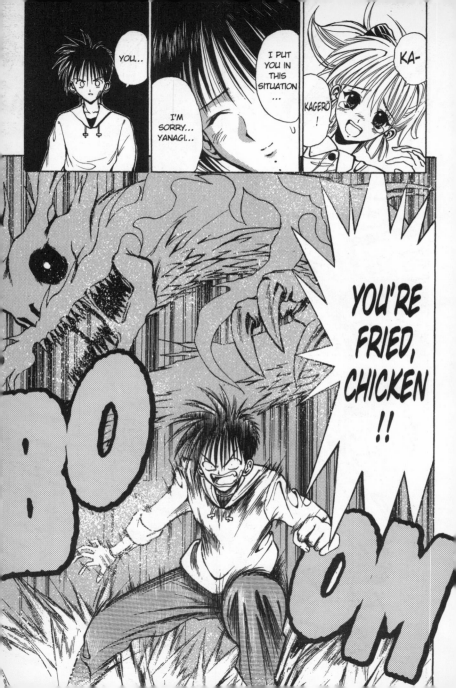

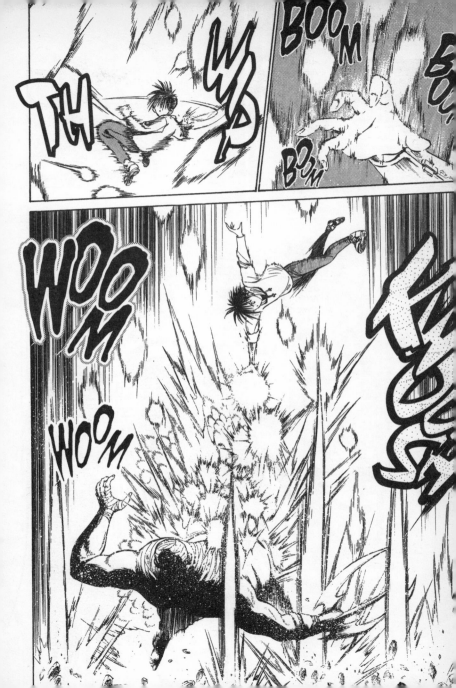

THAT I WISHED FOR YOU TO KILL ME?

I'M FINE... YANAGI CAN HEAL ME...

DO YOU REMEMBER? RECCA ....

IT MUST HURT EVEN IF YOU CAN'T DIE!!

ARE YOU OKAY, MOTHER !!

TO URUHA ...

F·NU·MP...

VICTORY ...

BUT NOW... THINGS HAVE CHANGED....

IT WAS MY WISH TO BE CONSUMED BY THE FLAMES OF MY OWN SON ...

I WAS TIRED OF LIVING....

I WANTED YOU TO KILL ME....

I COULDN'T DIE... I WANTED TO DIE...

I'M VERY HAPPY, RECCA, BECAUSE ...

YOU CALLED ME "MOTHER."

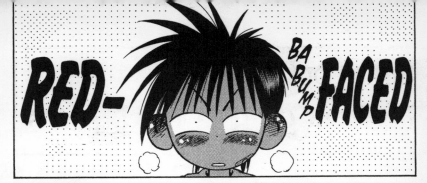

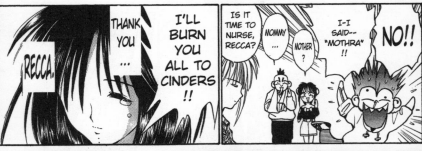

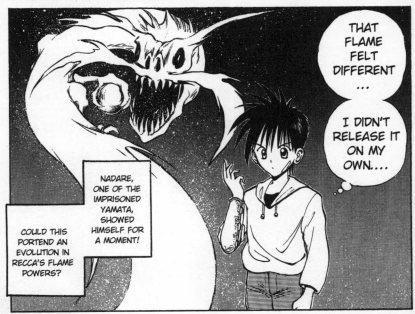

Part Forty-One: Challenge of the Eight Dragons

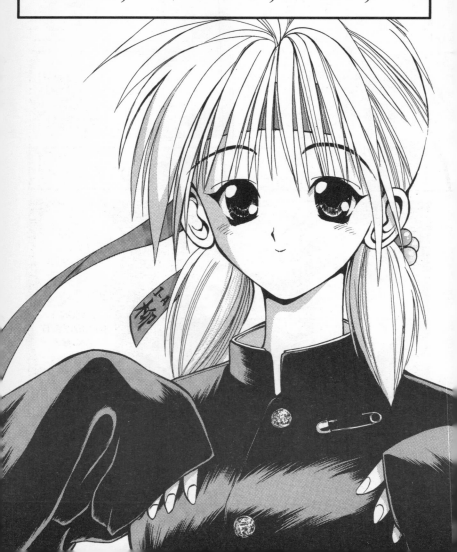

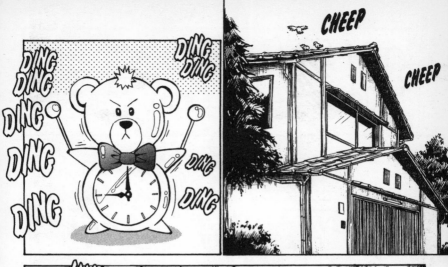

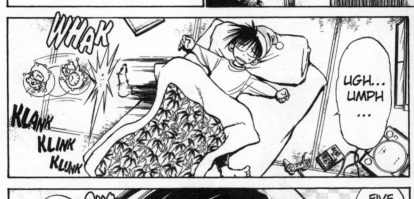

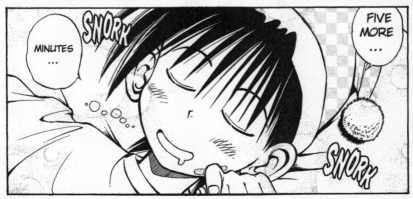

22

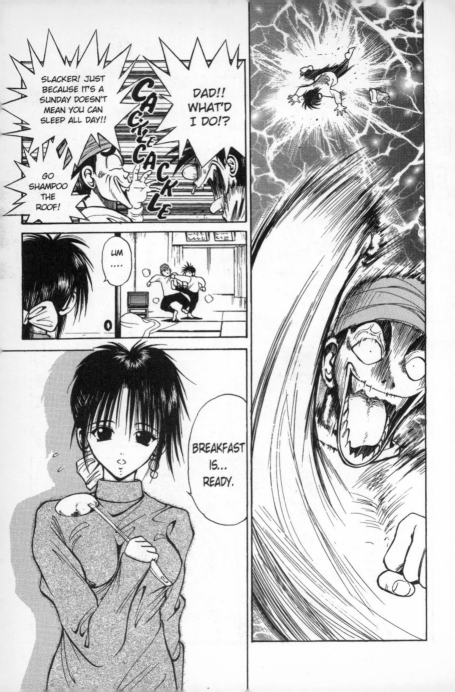

I NEVER HAD A MOTHER BEFORE ...

BUT ... HMPH. JERK.

UM ...

LET'S LEAVE THAT IDIOT ALONE, SHALL WE?

OH! HOW KIND OF YOU, MS. KAGERŌ! YOU SHOULDN'T HAVE!

WHAK

THIS ISN'T SO BAD ...

OINK OINK

OINK

ER... THERE'S ENOUGH FOR EVERYONE.

24

KEEP THOSE HORMONES IN CHECK, BOY! ♡

A DATE THIS EARLY?

PRINCESS!! ♡

GOOD MORNING!

WATCH OUT FOR CARS.

↑ HER BABY

YOU KEEP YOUR HANDS OFF MY MOTHER, SICKO!

I'M OFF! BREAKFAST WAS DELICIOUS!

FSSSS

SO ...

...

FRANKLY, I FEEL DUPED.

THAT FOOL TOLD ME THE WHOLE STORY.

CARING FOR HIM ALL THESE YEARS.

I'M SO GRATEFUL TO YOU FOR

THAT'S OKAY!!

PERHAPS I HAVE NO RIGHT TO CALL MYSELF HIS MOTHER NOW.

HE'S STILL YOUR SON,

AND YOU HAVE NO REASON TO FEEL INDEBTED TO ME!

GEEZ, LADY, PLEASE DON'T CRY! I CAN'T STAND TO SEE A WOMAN WEEP.

THAT I FOUND HIM...

IT WAS 15 YEARS AGO, ON A RAINY DAY...

I WAS A BACHELOR. IT WAS LIKE A LITTLE CRYING, CRAPPING HURRICANE HAD HIT MY LIFE!

SO I BECAME HIS FATHER.

RECCA ...

AN ABANDONED CHILD...

...

THAT'S JUST A MOVIE STAR I LIKED!!

HE'S SO CLUELESS, HE'LL NEVER NOTICE!!

OH THAT!?

HUH?

BUT YOU WERE MARRIED... THAT PHOTO ...

BACHELOR ?

REMINDS ME OF OKA.

THIS MAN ...

IF THAT'S HOW HE WANTS IT, WHERE'S THE PROBLEM?

HE'S 16 ... OLD ENOUGH TO DECIDED FOR HIMSELF.

HE STILL SEEMS TO THINK OF ME AS HIS FATHER.

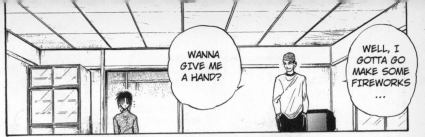

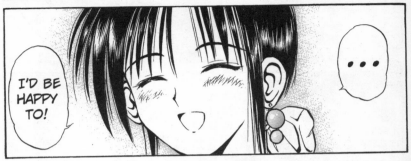

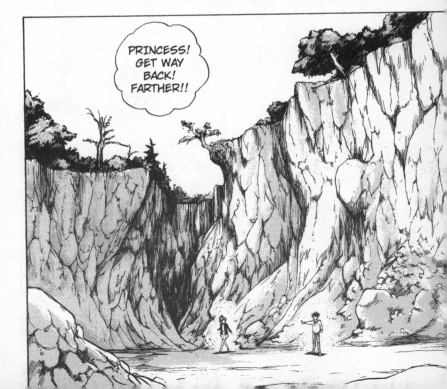

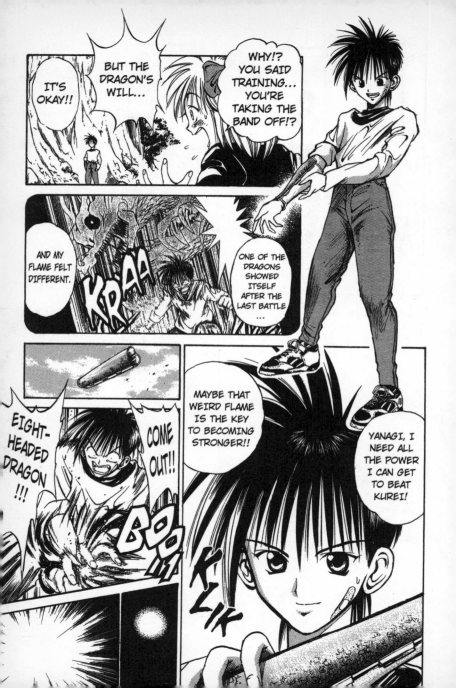

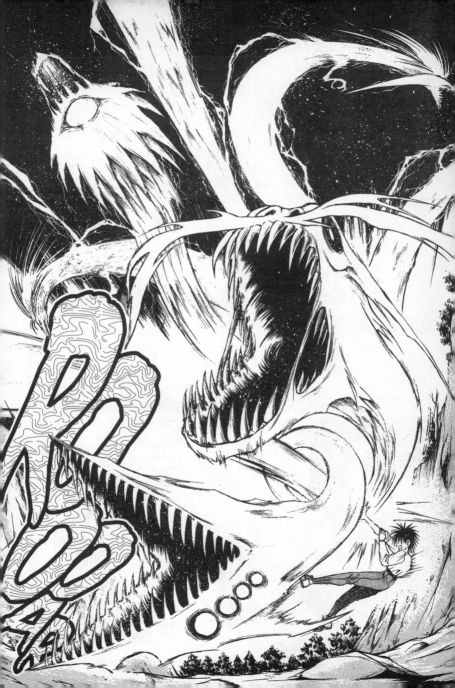

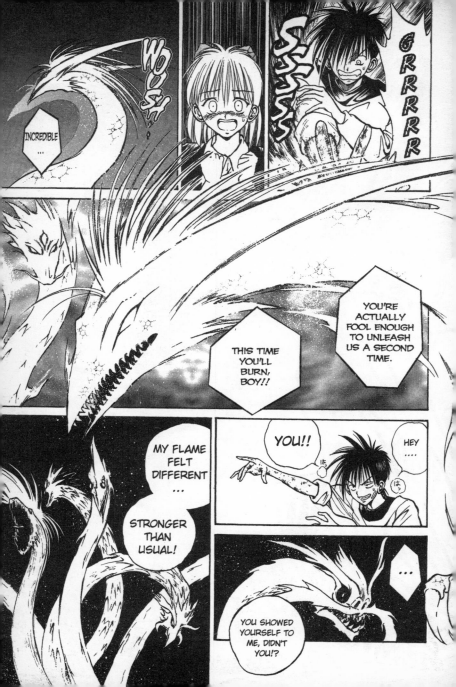

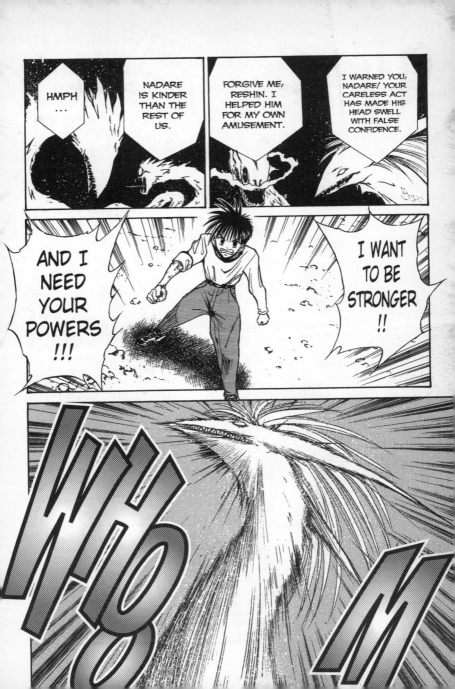

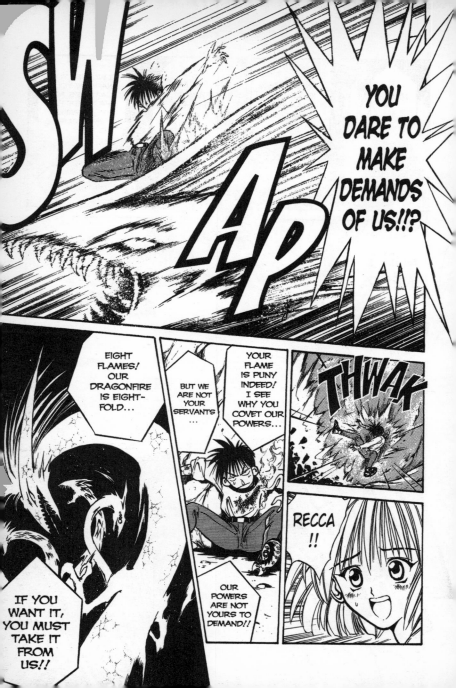

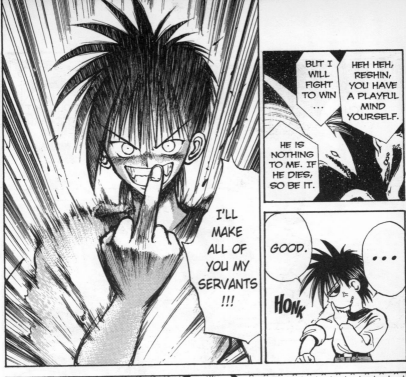

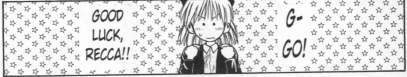

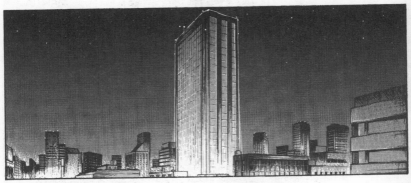

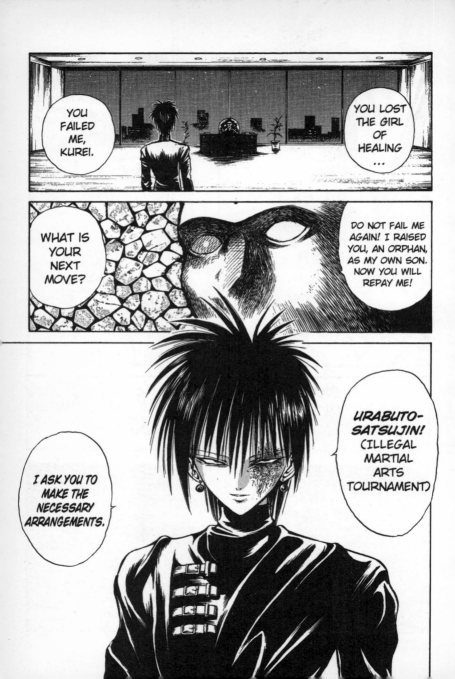

URABUTOSATSUJIN-- AN ILLEGAL MARTIAL ARTS TOURNAMENT. HUGE SUMS OF MONEY ARE WAGERED ON DEADLY BATTLES.

HMM... THE BATTLE TOURNAMENT...

THERE'S MONEY TO BE MADE.

BUT IF SHE WERE PUT UP AS A WAGER...

WE CAN CAPTURE THE GIRL OF HEALING, BUT HOLDING HER IS ANOTHER MATTER.

I CAN'T WAIT TO SEE THEM AGAIN.

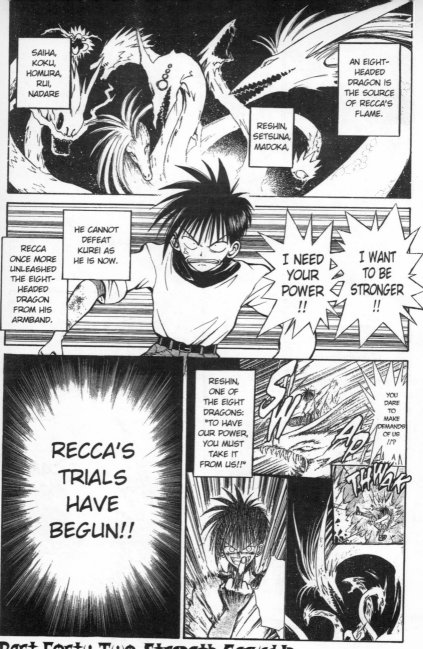

Part Forty-Two: Strength Carved In

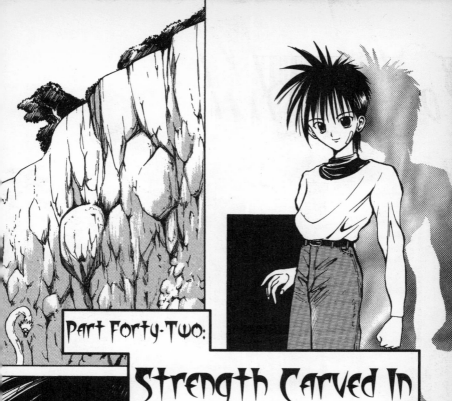

Part Forty-Two:

Strength Carved In

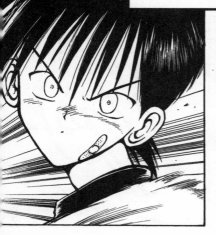

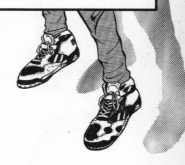

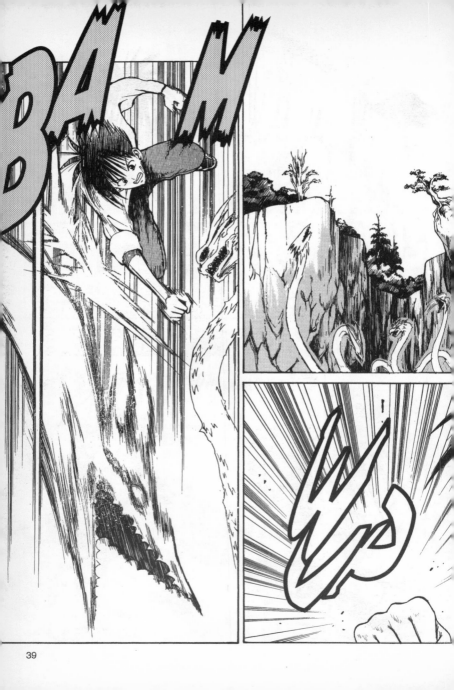

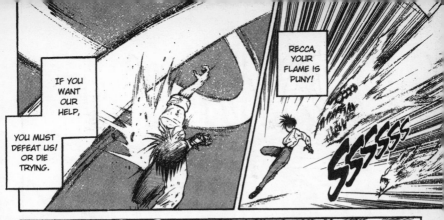

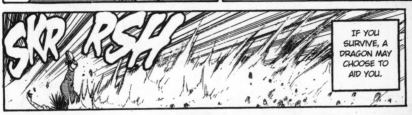

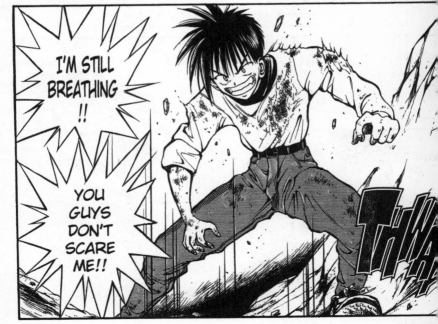

RECCA !!

WIN ...

I'LL CUT YOUR ALLOWANCE!

I'M ENTERTAINING A GUEST!!

DO I LOOK LIKE A FLOWER-SELLER!!

DOMON! WHERE ARE YOU!?

Ishijima Flowers

WHAT'S UP?

IT'S AN HONOR TO HAVE YOU IN MY HOME.

WHAM

RATS !

HELP OUT IN STORE FOR ONCE!

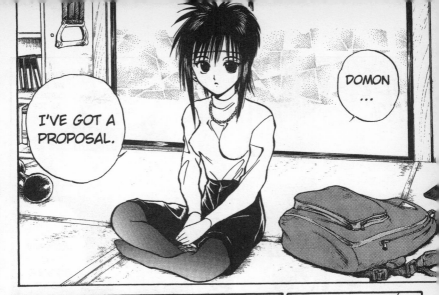

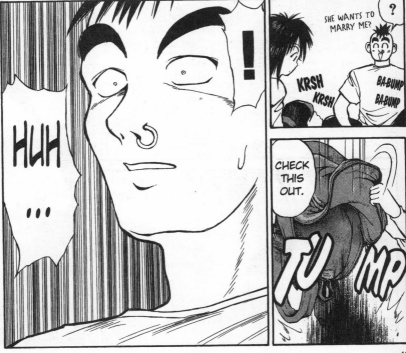

DOMON, WE BOTH CLAIM TO BE TOP DOG,

BUT WE WERE LIKE FAT PUPS NEXT TO KUREI.

I SAY WE GET STRONGER TOGETHER!

I'M NOBODY'S *SIDEKICK*!

DOESN'T THAT BOTHER YOU?

WITH THESE?

...

IF WE'RE GONNA BE RECCA'S RIVALS, WE GOTTA BE AS STRONG AS HE IS.

OKAY!

...

MANY DAYS LATER ...

AND SO ...

MAKING ME LIE, DARN IT ...

GOOD LUCK!

GUYS!!

UH... THEY CONTRACTED...

THE MUMPS.

ARE THEY IN REFORM SCHOOL, OR SOMETHING?

MR. TATESAKO, HANABISHI AND HIS GANG HAVEN'T BEEN TO SCHOOL FOR A WHILE NOW.

WOW...

TAKE A LOOK AT THIS PLACE.

44

WHAT'S A DOG DOING HERE!?

WOOF WOOF

HMM?

I HEARD RECCA WAS TRAINING HERE.

WOOF

TMP TMP TMP

OOH! ♡ HE'S CUTE! ♡

DON'T TOUCH IT!

PANT PANT

PANT

PANT

IS EVERYONE TRAINING HERE?

TOKIYA!

FUKO!!

THAT'S NO ORDINARY DOG.

KWEEEEE

MESSAGE. I HAVE A MESSAGE FOR YOU...

FROM MASTER KUREI'S...

PANT

PANT

PANT

IT'S PROBABLY *KUCHI-YOSE*-- VOICE CARRIER.

IT'S AN OLD NINJA TRICK FOR TALKING AT A DISTANCE BY MANIPULATING ANOTHER PERSON.

TALKED !?

THE DOG!?

WUMP

I COULD KILL ALL OF YOU ANY TIME I CHOOSE. BUT THAT WOULD NOT SATISFY ME!

THEREFORE, I INVITE ALL OF YOU TO THE URABUTOSATSWIN MARTIAL ARTS TOURNAMENT! YOU WILL BE NOTIFIED OF THE TIME AND LOCATION.

THE PENALTY FOR REFUSING TO COMPETE... IS DEATH!!

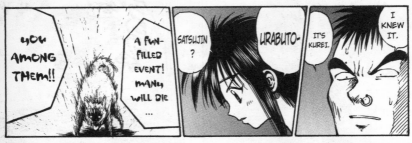

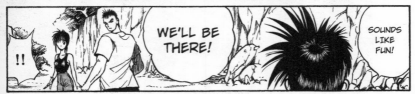

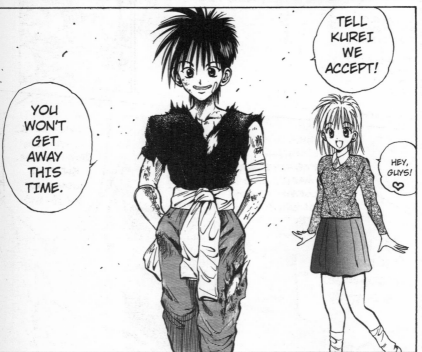

THIS? HA HA HA!

A SIGN OF MANHOOD.

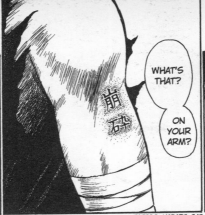

WHAT'S THAT?

ON YOUR ARM?

UH... RECCA?

TATTOO: NADARE SAI

THE OTHER SIX STILL NEED SOME PERSUADING.

I GOT TWO OF 'EM!

HOW DARE YOU SPEAK TO MASTER KUREI LIKE THAT!!

?

YOU SHALL DIE NOW!!!

WHAT ARE YOU TALKING ABOUT?

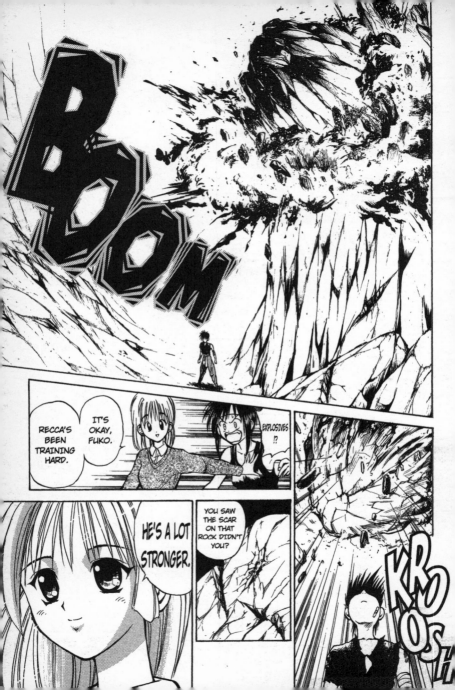

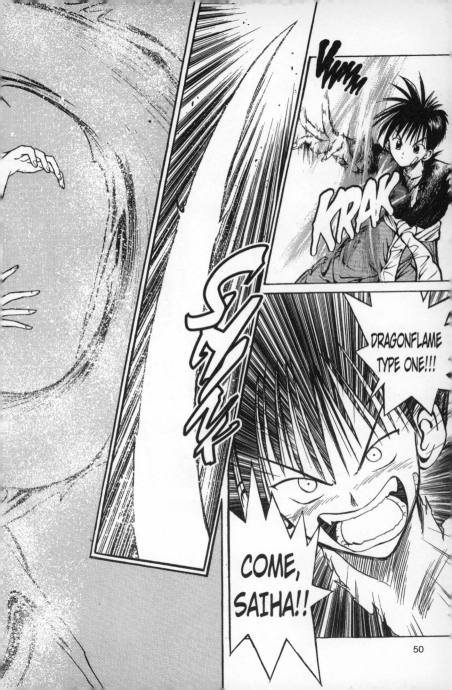

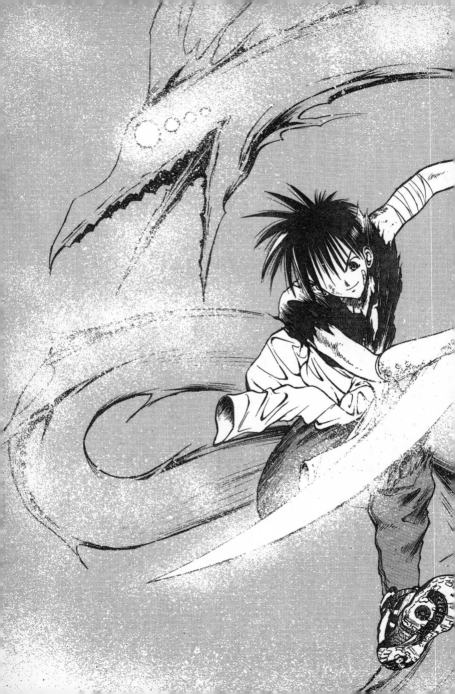

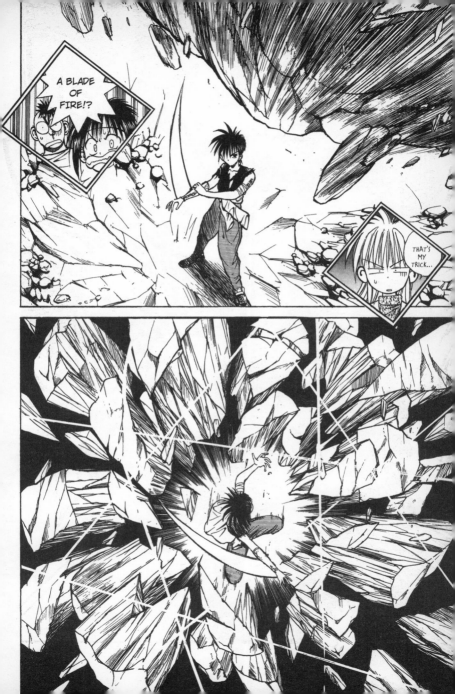

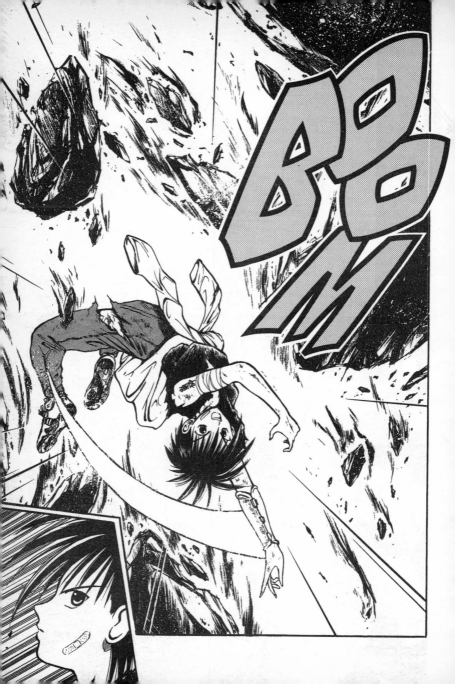

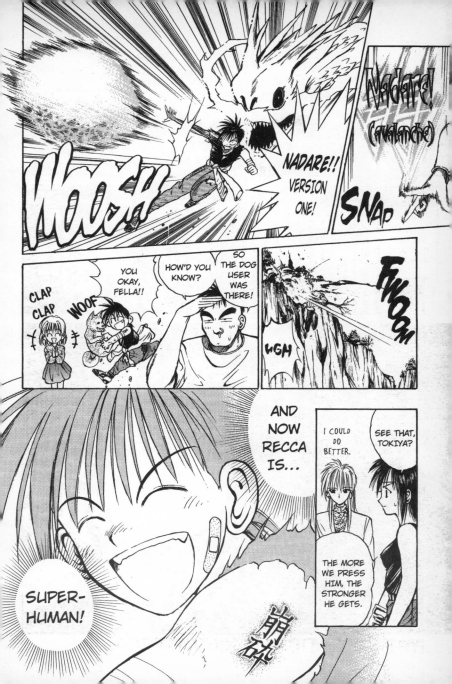

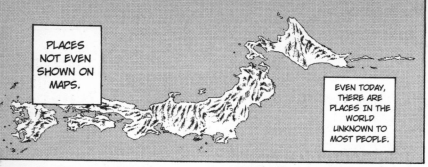

EVEN TODAY, THERE ARE PLACES IN THE WORLD UNKNOWN TO MOST PEOPLE.

PLACES NOT EVEN SHOWN ON MAPS.

IT IS LABELED ONLY AS "PRIVATE PROPERTY."

WARNING

C PREFECTURE

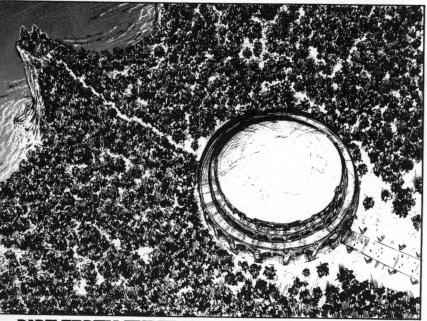

PART FORTY-THREE: URABUTOSATSUJIN

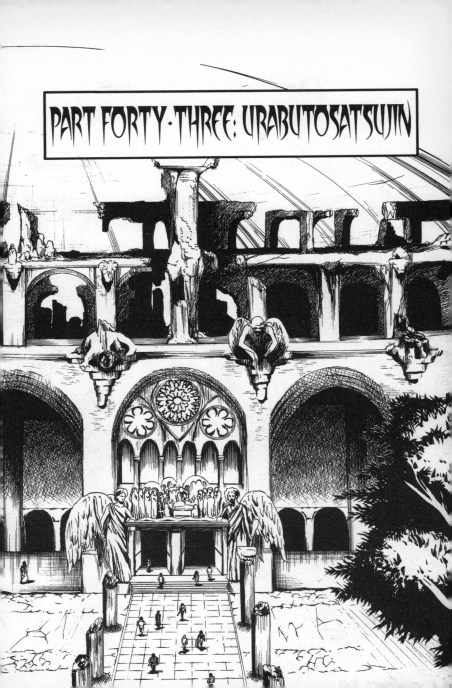
PART FORTY·THREE: URABUTOSATSUJIN

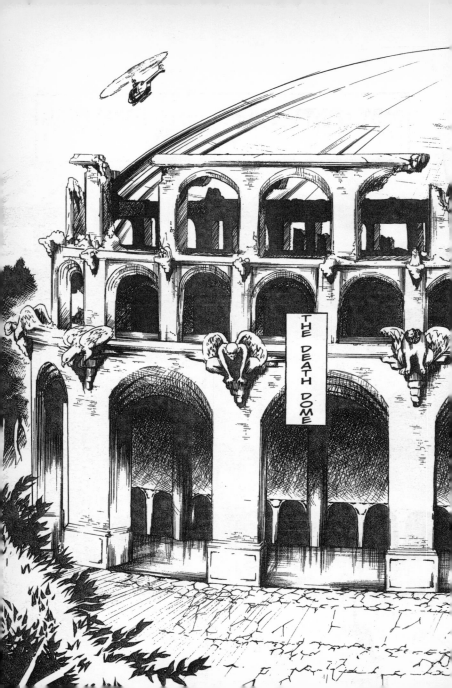

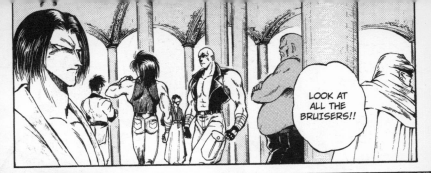

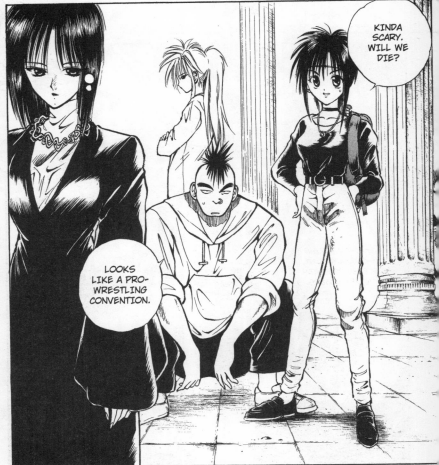

GETTING COLD FEET?

THEY MAY LOOK LIKE PEPPERS, BUT THEY'RE ONLY PUMPKINS!!

HE'S TOO STUPID TO FEEL FEAR.

HE'S IN GOOD SPIRITS....

I WANT APRICOT CANDY.

YAY!

ARE YOU HUNGRY, PRINCESS? I HOPE THEY'RE SELLING BATTERED OCTOPUS!

YIPPEE

TEAMS ENTERING THE TOURNAMENT, PLEASE REGISTER YOUR MEMBERS.

B-6

© RECCA HANABISHI
FUKO KIRISAWA
DOMON ISHIJIMA
TOKIYA MIKAGAMI

RECCA HANABISHI?

TEAM LEADER...

WELCOME TO THE BATTLE FESTIVAL! THANK YOU FOR COMING.

HANABISHI... YOU MUST BE THE MR. HANABISHI MASTER KUREI MENTIONED?

HEH HEE HEE HEE...

HEH HEH...

CERTAINLY.

WILL KUREI BE IN THIS TOURNAMENT?

HEY, BUDDY.

MASTER KUREI?

BATTLES WILL TAKE PLACE IN A TOURNAMENT FORMAT...

TEAMS WILL BE COMPETING AGAINST EACH OTHER. EACH TEAM CAN HAVE UP TO FIVE MEMBERS. FEWER IS ACCEPTABLE.

ALLOW ME TO EXPLAIN THE RULES.

IT IS EVERYBODY'S FIRST TIME AT THE *URABUTOSATSUJIN*, CORRECT?

WHATEVER HAPPENS, YOU WILL HAVE NO LEGAL RECOURSE.

LET ME WARN YOU IN ADVANCE, THIS IS AN ILLEGAL TOURNAMENT.

URABUTOSATSUJIN ... I'VE HEARD RUMORS BUT I WASN'T SURE THAT KUREI WAS INVOLVED.

I DOUBT WE'LL COME THROUGH THIS UNSCATHED ...

DON'T WORRY, PRINCESS!

...

KRK...

DON'T WORRY, DOMON.

WIPE YOUR NOSE, BIG GUY.

KRK

...

YOUR WEAPONS ARE NO EXCEPTIONS.

THE LOSERS' WEAPONS BECOME PRIZES TO THE VICTORS!

THIS TOURNAMENT ALLOWS THE USE OF ALL WEAPONS... INCLUDING THE *MADOGU!!*

LET ME CONTINUE.

A SIDE BENEFIT OF THE TOURNAMENT.

THIS MUST BE HOW KUREI COLLECTED THE SCATTERED TALISMANS!

I SEE.

FINALLY, IF THE TEAM IS DEFEATED ...

YOU MUST SURRENDER SOMETHING VALUABLE AS TRIBUTE TO THE HOST!!

THE MORE PRECIOUS YOUR WAGER, THE HARDER YOU WILL FIGHT.

THOSE ARE THE RULES...

WHAT A RACKET!!

THAT STINKS! WE GOTTA PAY TO LOSE?

HUH?

LET'S SEE...

PRO WRESTLER YOJI ANJO'S T-SHIRT....

UNACCEPTABLE.

ALL RIGHT!!

THE RIGHT TO FEEL MY BREASTS!

UNACCEPTABLE.

HOW ABOUT YOU?

MOM, GEEZ!

MY B-BREASTS?

HOW EMBARRASSING.

FORGET IT, IGOR!!

M-MY BREASTS?

SOME HAVE PUT UP THEIR FRIENDS, THEIR PARENTS, EVEN THEIR LOVERS.

OTHER TEAMS ARE PUTTING UP PEOPLE AS WAGER.

IT'S NOT UNUSUAL.

I'LL DO IT!!

I'LL BE THE WAGER!!

IF YOU CAN'T BEAR TO LOSE IT, THEN KEEP WINNING!!

THESE GAMES ARE NOT FOR CHILDREN. YOU MUST MAKE AN ACCEPTABLE WAGER!!

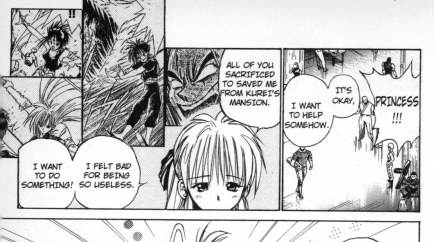

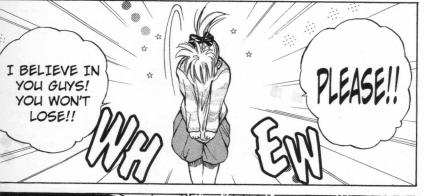

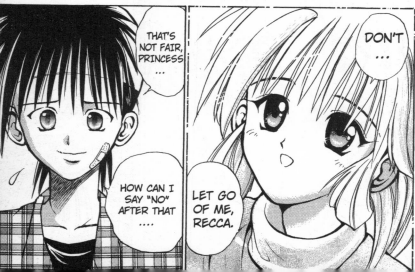

MASTER MORI, OUR PLAN WORKED PERFECTLY!!

HEE HEE HEE HEE...

LOOKS LIKE SHE'S GOT HER MIND SET ON THIS.

STUBBORN GIRL...

YANAGI'S ON THE LINE.

WELL, NOW WE CAN'T LOSE.

I SUSPECT THAT MAN WAS AFTER MIKAGAMI FAMILY'S HEIRLOOM, THE MADOGU ENSUI.

TOKIYA, I HEARD YOU WERE SEARCHING FOR THE MAN WHO KILLED YOUR SISTER.

NOW I'VE GOT TWO REASONS ...

THEY WERE LIKELY TALISMAN-WIELDERS WORKING FOR KUREI.

PERHAPS THEY WILL BE IN THIS TOURNAMENT.

WE'LL SHOW YOU LATER!

WE'VE GOT OUR SECRET WEAPONS!

HEH HEH

NO SWEAT!!

ARE YOU UP FOR THIS?

WHAT A QUESTION!

THE THRILL OF COMPETITION ...

REVENGE FOR TOKIYA!

HEY!!

REASONS TO FIGHT--

FUKO'S GOOD, BUT DOMON?

FOR PRINCESS ...

AND ONE MORE THING.

AND FOR ME...

A TALISMAN THAT'LL ALLOW HER TO AGE NORMALLY...

MAYBE ONE OF THOSE TALISMANS CAN BREAK THE CURSE ON MOM...

WE GET TO KEEP THE WEAPONS AND TALISMANS OF THE LOSERS...

MOM ...

TO SEE IF YOU ARE WORTHY TO PARTICIPATE IN THIS TOURNAMENT.

NOW THEN...

SWAP

TIME TO CONDUCT A TEST...

68

I CAN'T QUITE BELIEVE ...

THAT THIS MOTLEY CREW FOUGHT MASTER KUREI AND HIS ASSASSINS TO A DRAW!

KILL 'EM ALL!!

THEY ALWAYS HAVE TO LEARN THE HARD WAY.

GOOD! I WAS GETTING TIRED OF LOOKING AT HIS HIDEOUS FACE.

CH.K.

UGLY PIG!

SPLASH

I SAW.

MASTER KUREI, THEY'VE ARRIVED.

THEY BEAT 20 MEN IN 15 SECONDS.

FINALLY A CHALLENGE.

HOW THRILLING.

AND EACH FIGHTER HAS A UNIQUE PERSONAL REASON.

TEAM RECCA ENTERS THE *URABUTO-SATSUJIN* ...

THAT'LL SHOW 'EM.

THEY'RE TOUGH ....

NOT THAT TOUGH ...

MOST OF US COULD DO THE SAME ...

DID YOU SEE THAT?

FWUMP

HMPH. FINE, YOU PASS ...

BUT DON'T THINK THIS MEANS YOU CAN WIN.

AND DEFEAT IS NOT AN OPTION!

FEARSOME ENEMIES ABOUND.

A NEW CHAPTER OF BATTLE HAS BEGUN!!

72

PART FORTY-FOUR:
THE BATTLE TOURNAMENT OPENS

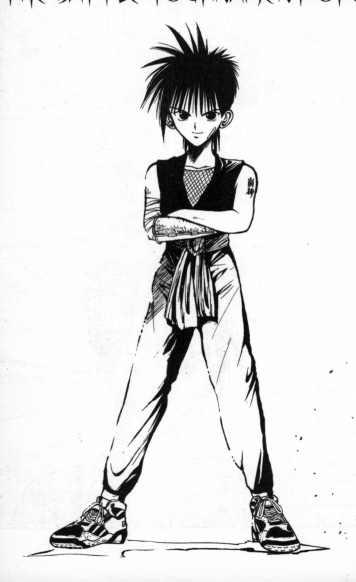

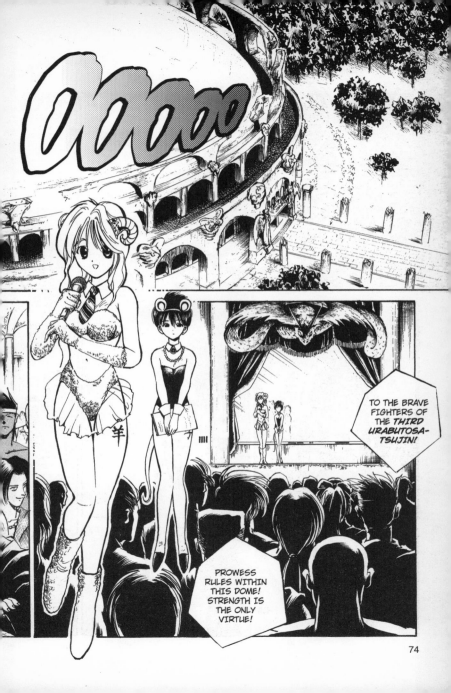

74

I HATE SPEECHES.

BO-RING!

YAWN

PATIENCE, SQUIRMY.

DO YOURSELVES PROUD!

LET THE WINNER TAKE ALL.

HUH?

I'M WITH THE KID!!

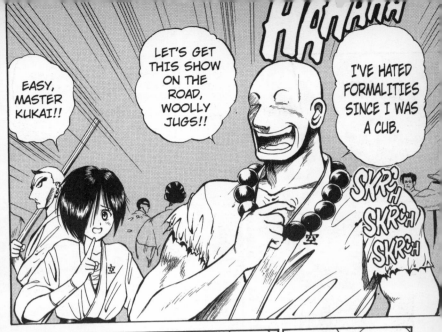

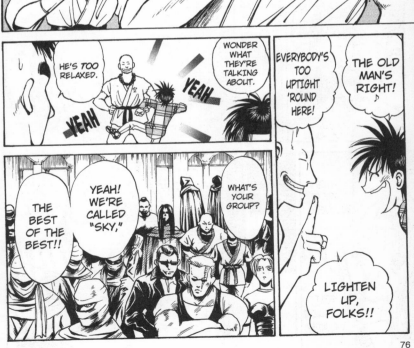

MASTER!!

OKAY OKAY

BUT AFTER THIS, EVERYONE WILL KNOW US!

WE'RE STILL UNKNOWN.

HA HA,

NEVER HEARD OF IT.

WA HA HA HA

WHAT'S WRONG?

...

GOOD LUCK!

MAYBE WE'LL FACE EACH OTHER LATER!

!

KRUNCH

AND NOW A WORD OF ENCOURAGEMENT

FROM THE TOURNAMENT ORGANIZER!

HE'S NO ORDINARY FIGHTER!!

I FELT A RABID BLOOD-LUST WHEN I TOUCHED HIM!

LIGHTEN UP? HOW...

THAT OLD MAN...

VOOON...

BLAH BLAH

I AM YOUR HOST, MORI KŌRAN!

WELCOME, WARRIORS!!

OH...

I'VE SEEN HIM SOMEWHERE BEFORE...

HMM?

PUBLICLY, HE PRETENDS TO BE A PHILANTHROPIST BUT...

HE'S THE BIGGEST AND BADDEST OF 'EM ALL!

BLAB

SO THAT'S...

IT'S KŌRAN....

THE LORD OF THE UNDERWORLD....

BLAB

EEEEEK!!

YOU THINK HE'S UGLY?

HE'S CREEPY!

HA HA HA HA

WHAT A WEIRD FACE!!

BUT TO GET THEM, YOU MUST WIN!

LET THE GAMES BEGIN!!

THE WINNERS WILL RECEIVE WORTHY PRIZES.

I WISH ALL OF YOU LUCK.

YAY

POWER WOMEN,...

MONEY...

79

YEAH...

IT'S TIME.

BLONDIE!

SAME TO YOU,

DON'T HOLD ME BACK.

I'LL FIGHT BESIDE YOU GUYS BECAUSE IT'S THE RULES, BUT...

80

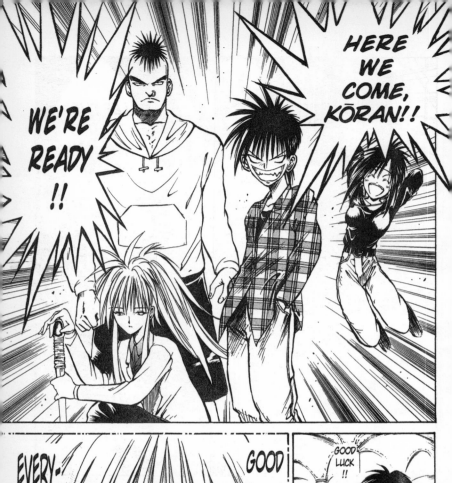

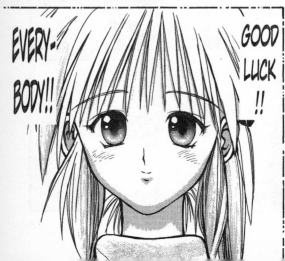

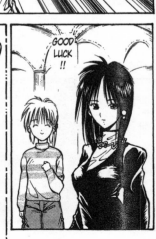

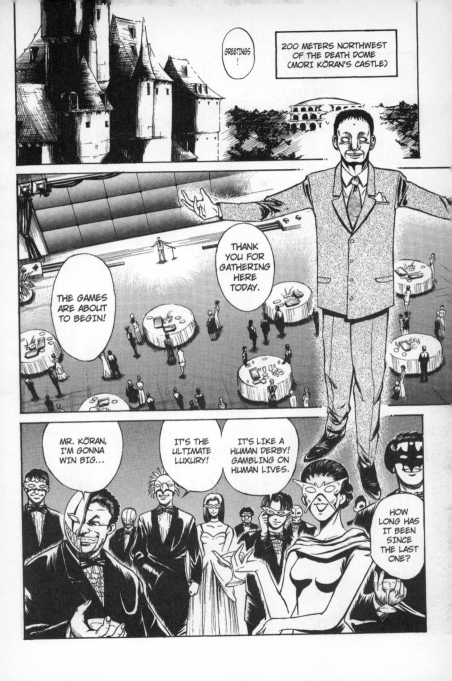

THIS GROUP COULD PROVE SURPRISINGLY DIFFICULT.

PARTICULARLY...

HE WILL FACE A FORMIDABLE GROUP THIS TIME.

NO...

YOUR OWN SON KUREI IS THE FAVORITE, NO?

BE MINE !!

SHE WILL...

THE GIRL OF HEAL- ING !!

HEH HEH, HERE THEY CAME... AND WITH THEM...

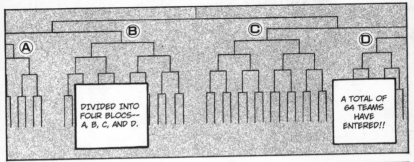

DIVIDED INTO FOUR BLOCS-- A, B, C, AND D.

A TOTAL OF 64 TEAMS HAVE ENTERED!!

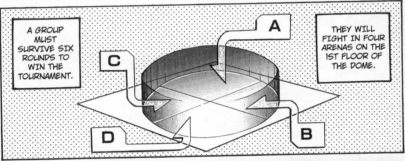

A GROUP MUST SURVIVE SIX ROUNDS TO WIN THE TOURNAMENT.

THEY WILL FIGHT IN FOUR ARENAS ON THE 1ST FLOOR OF THE DOME.

RECCA'S PLACE OF BATTLE WAS...

SO THIS IS OUR BATTLEFIELD.

I SEE YOU'VE CHANGED.

84

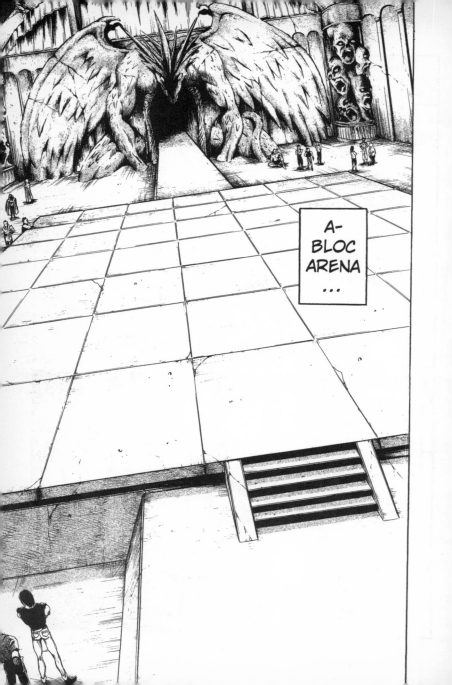

A-BLOC ARENA ...

SUCKS?! I'D SAY WE'RE LUCKY!!

THAT SUCKS!

LOOKS LIKE KUREI'S TEAM ISN'T IN OUR BLOC.

OVER-CONFIDENT FOOL...

HMPH

RECCA HANABISHI'S TEAM HOKAGE!!

TADA

LET'S STAR THE FIRS ROUND O A-BLOC, FIRST OF IS...

I COULD BEAT THEM BY MYSELF!!

MAN, THE OTHER TEAM IS SO LUCKY!

HA! MISS YOUR MOMMIES !?

DEAD MEAT !!!

SO SOON?

YOU NAMED US "HOKAGE?"

BUNCH OF KIDS... THEY WON'T SURVIVE THE FIRST ROUND!

NEVER HEARD OF 'EM.

HOKAGE?

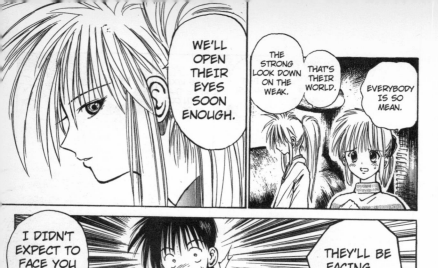

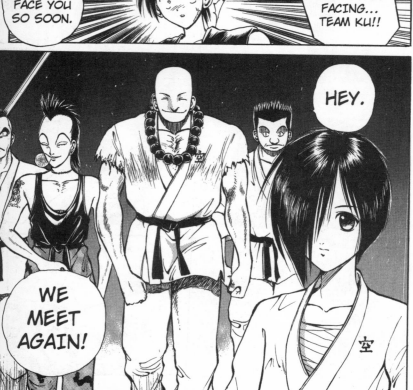

THIS IS WHERE KU'S LEGEND BEGINS.

LET'S MAKE IT A GOOD FIGHT!

THE MOST FEARED MURDERERS IN THE NORTHEAST!!

IT'S KU, THEY'RE AN UNDERWORLD HIT-SQUAD!!

SAICHO, TOO!!

IT'S "KUKAI THE MERCIFUL!!"

KUKAI...

CHATTER

I KNEW IT!

I KNEW THERE WAS SOMETHING SPECIAL ABOUT HIM!!

UNLIKE US.

OUR OPPONENTS HAVE A REPUTATION.

HOW RUDE

PREPARE FOR BATTLE!!

TEAMS TO THE RING!!

A BLOC 1ST MATCH TEAMS

KU	HOKAGE

DAIKOKU — **SENPO (1ST)** — TOKIYA MIKAGAMI

MINAMIO — **JIHO (2ND)** — DOMON ISHIJIMA

FUJIMARU — **CHUKEN (3RD)** — FUKO KIRISAWA

SAICHO — **FUKUSHO (4TH)** — RECCA HANABISHI

KUKAI — **TAISHO (5TH)** — TO BE DECIDED LATER.

89

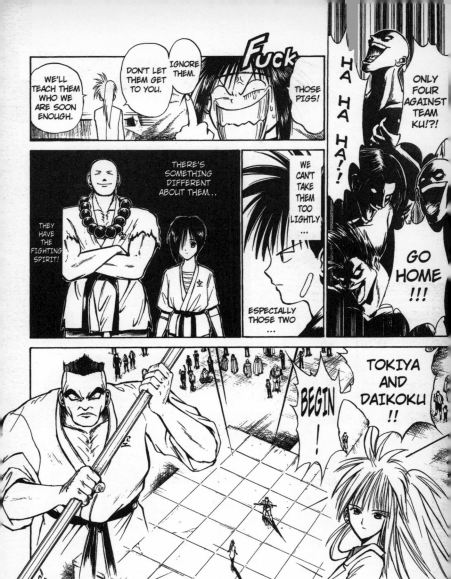

YOU'VE MASTERED THE HYOMON-KEN--THE ICE CREST SWORD....

TOKIYA, I HAVE NOTHING MORE TO TEACH YOU.

NO.

YOUR INTENTIONS STILL HAVE NOT CHANGED?

IT'S BEEN SEVEN YEARS SINCE I STARTED TEACHING YOU...

1

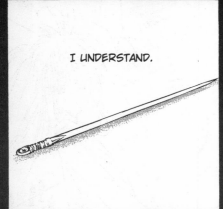

I UNDERSTAND.

ONE DAY, YOU'RE SURE TO STUMBLE ...

REVENGE ... THE SWORD WHICH SEEKS BLOOD FOLLOWS A ROCKY PATH!

MATCH 1 (HYOMON-KEN)

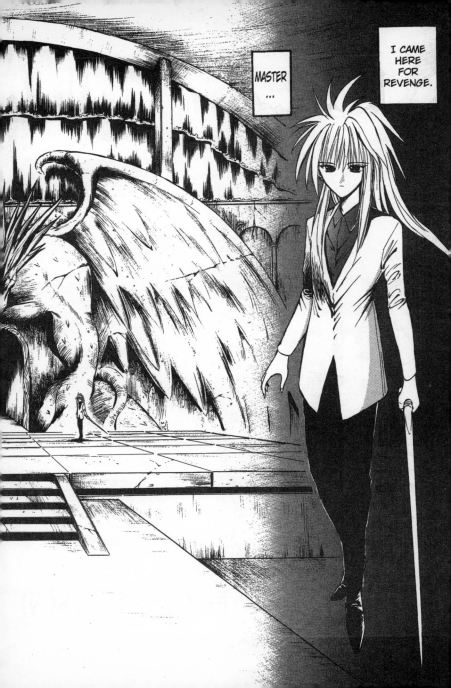

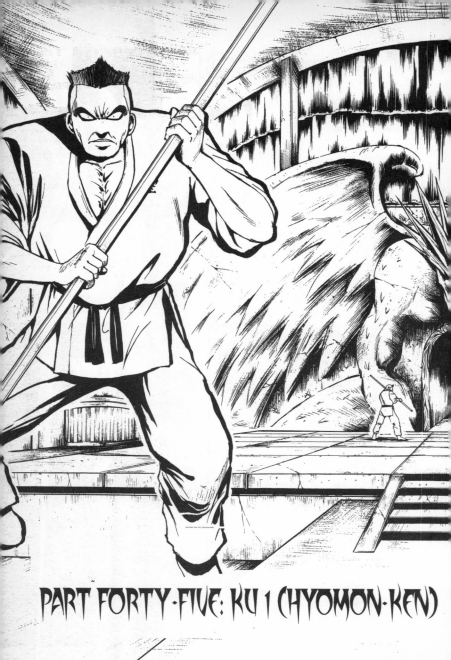

PART FORTY·FIVE: KU 1 (CHYOMON·KEN)

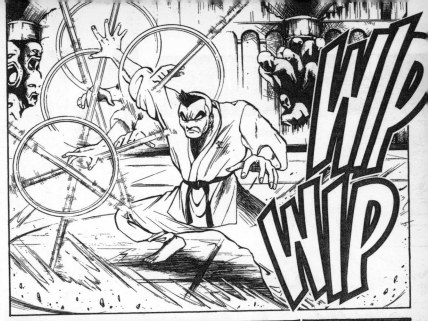

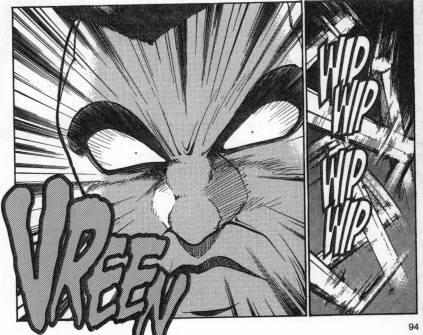

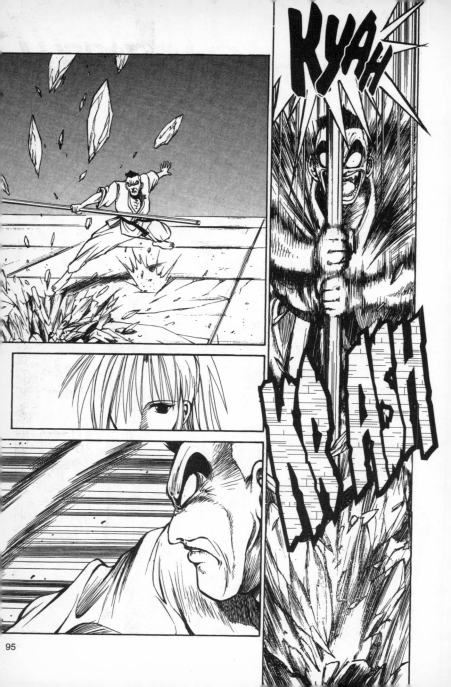

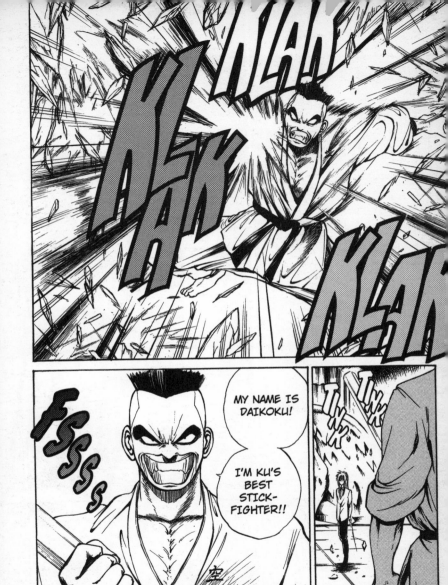

MY NAME IS DAIKOKU!

I'M KU'S BEST STICK-FIGHTER!!

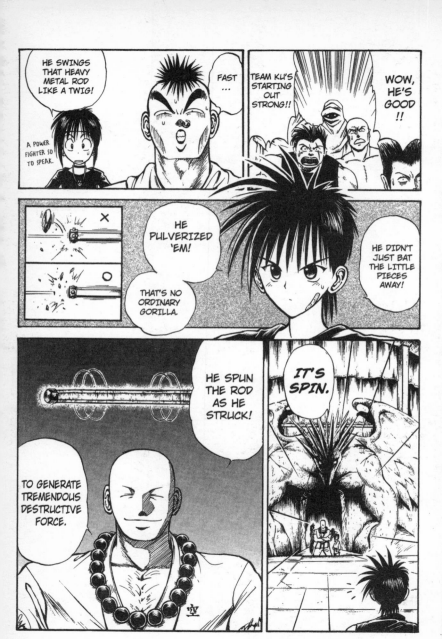

ONE BLOW WILL MAKE A BIG HOLE IN THAT SKINNY BOY!

JUST ANOTHER CIRCUS TRICK.

THEN YOU'RE IN FOR A BIG SURPRISE!!

YOU THINK YOU CAN TAKE ME, TOKIYA!?

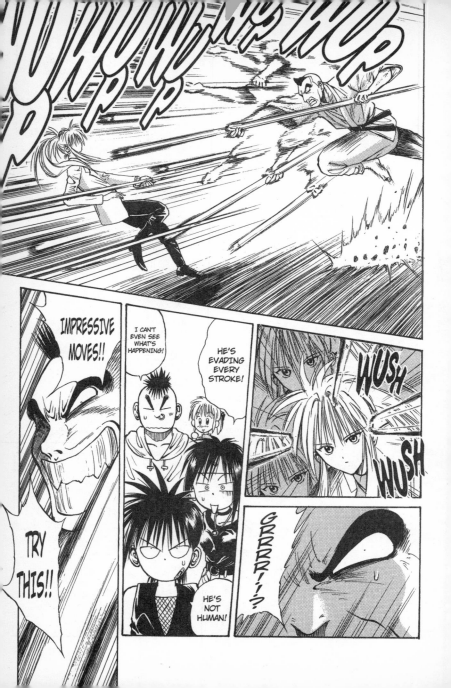

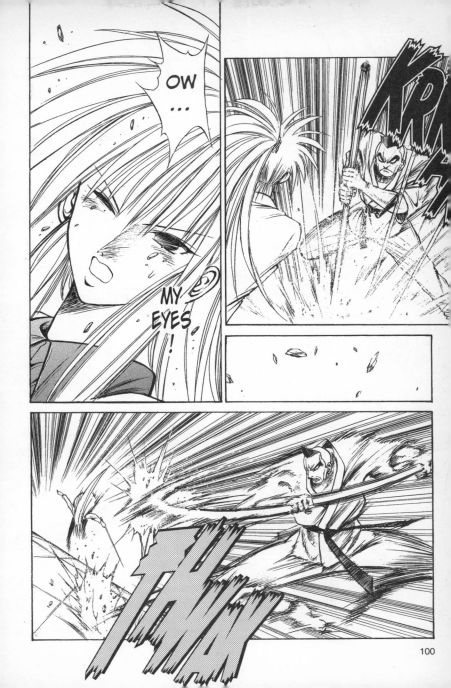

OW
...

MY
EYES
!

100

POP

TOKIYA!!

SKRFF

YIKES!!

HEY...

YOU ALIVE?

YOUR LEG!!?

THANK GOD YOU'RE ALIVE--BUT DON'T CALL ME A FLEA!

DON'T COUNT ME OUT, FIRE-FLEA.

HUH?

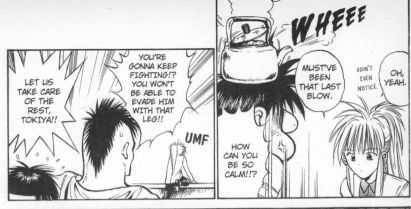

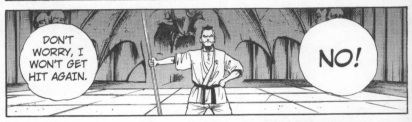

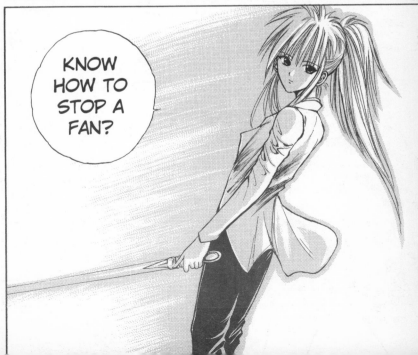

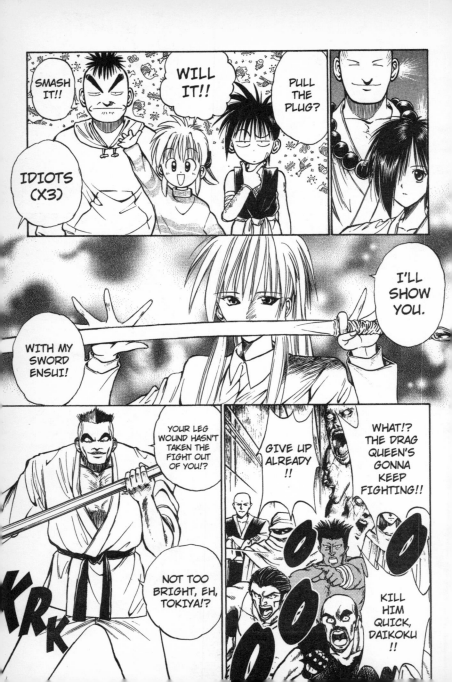

HYAAAAAH
WHOOSH
SWAP SWAP SWAP SWAP
HYAPON GEKI!! (ONE HUNDRED STRIKES)

EVERY BLOW !?

HE BLOCKED IT!!?

HUNH !?

(STICK)

(FAND

CENTER

IT WASN'T TO WILL IT.

THAT'S HOW YOU STOP A FAN...

AT THE CENTER !!

LET'S SEE YOU STOP THIS!!

PETTY TRICKERY !!

FWIP

TOKIYA MIKAGAMI !

YOU HAVE TO HOLD DOWN THE POINTY CENTER TO STOP IT COMPLETELY. IMPRESSIVE,

HIS SWORD, ENSUI, IS REMARKABLE --AND SO IS HIS SWORDS-MANSHIP!

I'VE SEEN THAT STYLE SOMEWHERE ...

KYUKYOKU SENBON GEKI!!! (ULTIMATE ONE THOUSAND STRIKES)

IT'S YOU WHO'S NOT TOO BRIGHT, DAIKOKU.

DID YOU THINK I'D EVADE YOU FOREVER?

THERE'S NOWHERE TO HIDE NOW!!

TO HIM, HIS OPPONENT'S ATTACKS ARE FROZEN! THE SWORD OF ICE... I DIDN'T KNOW ANYBODY COULD STILL WIELD THAT MAGIC SWORD!!

UGH...

NOW I REMEMBER!

THAT SWORD STYLE IS *HYOMON-KEN*, PASSED DOWN BY MEGURIKYOZA, THE SO-CALLED GOD OF SWORDS!!

ENSUI *FREEZES* THE MOVEMENT

OF MY OPPONENT!

HE MEMORIZED DAIKOKU'S MOVES FROM THE FIRST ATTACK! DAIKOKU MIGHT AS WELL HAVE BEEN STANDING STILL!

DAIKOKU HAS LOST.

YOU FOUGHT WELL,

BUT YOU'RE JUST A NORMAL HUMAN.

I'M BEATEN!?

BEATING YOU WAS CHILD'S PLAY.

PART FORTY-SIX:
KU 2 (LETHAL WEAPON)

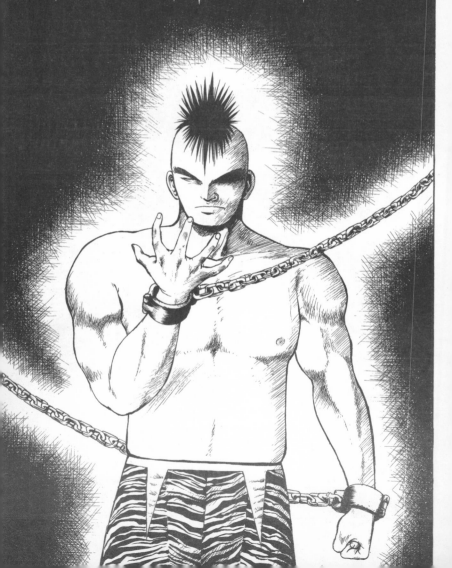

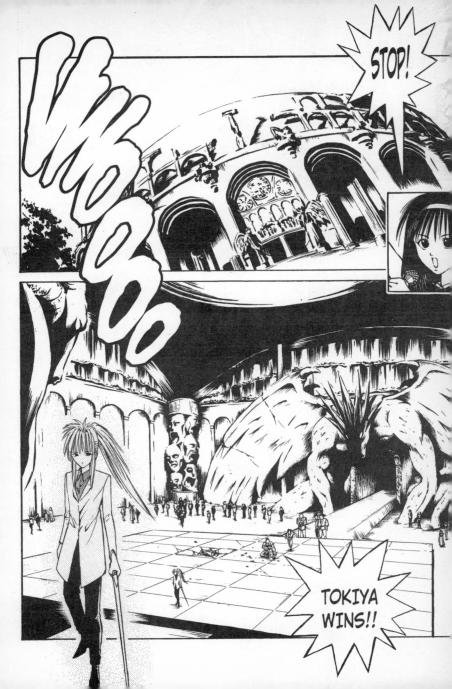

YEAH, TOKIYA !!

TOKIYA IS A VALUABLE ALLY, AS I'D HOPED.

IN NORMAL BATTLE, HE PROBABLY WOULD BE THE STRONGEST OF THE FOUR!

TOKIYA RULES!!

YIPEE!!

YIPEE!!

HOW EMBARRA-SSING.

YOU COULDN'T HELP IT. YOU WERE OUTMATCHED.

THE JIHO IS NEXT.

ARE YOU OKAY, DAIKOKU?

HE... HE'S NOT HUMAN!

HE WAS JUST A BLUR!

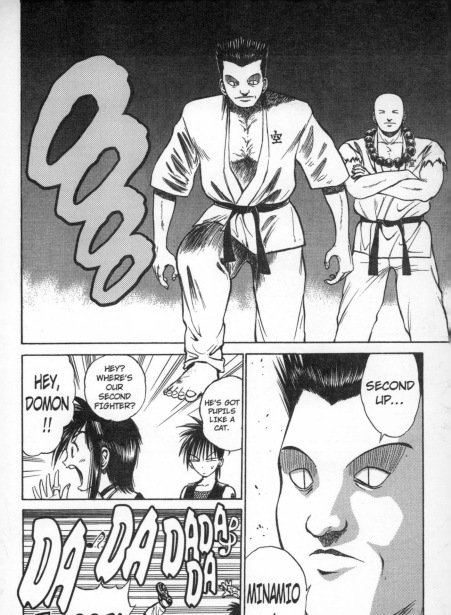

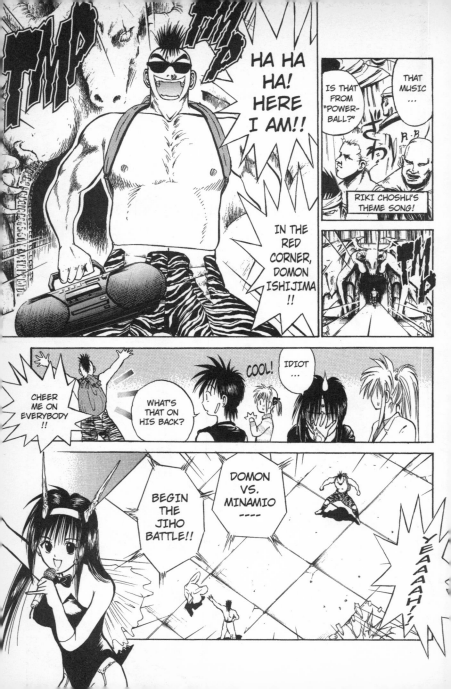

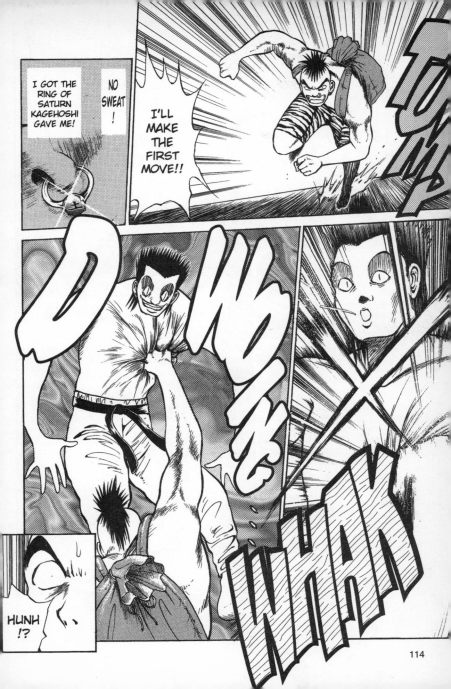

114

WHAT IS THIS GUY!?

YOU CALL YOURSELF STRONG?

YOU, THE WEAK LINK OF YOUR TEAM?

MY BODY IS LIKE RUBBER! YOUR PUNCHS CAN'T HURT ME!

WERRRP

HEY...

YOU TRYING TO HURT ME?

GWERK

YOU PUNCH LIKE A GIRL.

I'M GLAD I'M FIGHTING YOU INSTEAD OF TOKIYA.

IT'S LIKE PUNCHING A SPONGE.

THAT WAS THE SAME PUNCH THAT WRECKED SEKIO!?

DOMON'S PUNCH DIDN'T FAZE HIM!?

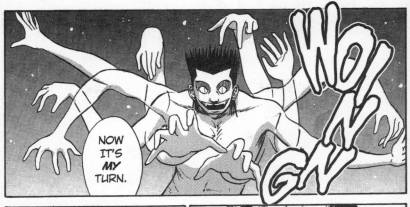

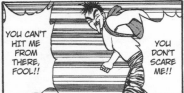

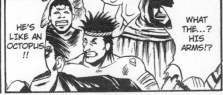

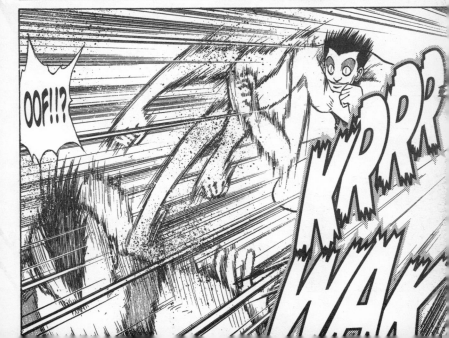

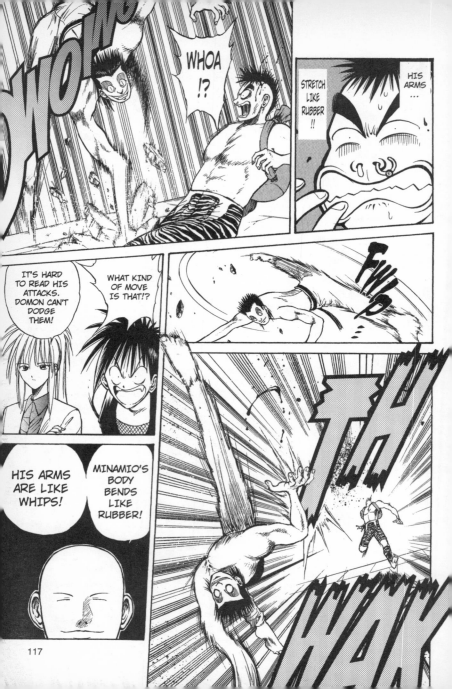

117

THEY GOT A WORD FOR PEOPLE LIKE YOU "DEAD WEIGHT"! OR WAS IT "MEAT"?

......!

THAT HUGE BODY IS USELESS!

GEEZ, YOU REALLY SUCK, FATTY!

WASTE THAT LUMMOX!!

AH HA HA! YOU TELL 'EM!!

FUKO...

SHUT YOUR TRAPS!!

TWITCH

118

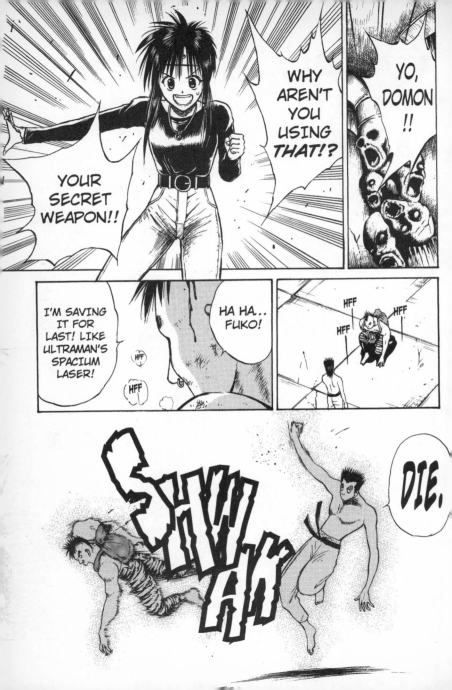

HIS OPPONENT IS UNABLE TO CONTINUE BATTLE...

MINAMIO WINS!

.....

THAT'S ENOUGH! STOP, DOMON!!

IF YOU KEEP FIGHTING HE'LL KILL YOU ...

NOT YET, DRAGON GIRL.

SKWEE

EEK

EEK

2:0

HE KNOWS WHAT HE'S DOING!

DON'T DISTRACT HIM, YANAGI...

WE CAN'T ASK HIM TO GIVE UP.

SNK

IF HE QUITS NOW, IT'LL RUIN HIS CONFIDENCE.

HE'S STRONGER THAN EVER!

I USED TO
THINK THAT
SOMETIMES
...

MAYBE
I'M NOT
AS
STRONG
AS
RECCA
OR
TOKIYA-

BUT...

WHA

YOU'RE
GOING
DOWN,
BIG
BOY!!

THWAP

SWAP

YOU'RE
WORTH-
LESS
AND
WEAK!!

THUNK

EVEN
YOUR
FRIENDS
HAVE
GIVEN
UP ON
YOU!!

LET'S
FIGHT,
RUBBER
MAN!

I AM STRONG!!!

I'D
LOSE
WHEN I
THOUGHT
LIKE
THAT!

TOMP

BELIEVE
IN
YOURSELF
!!

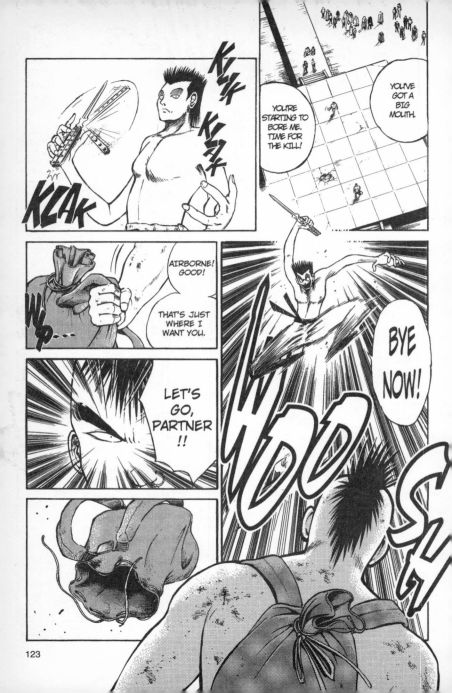

123

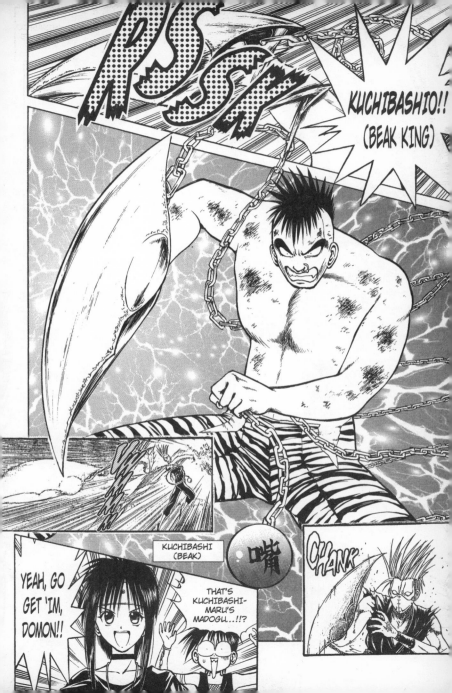

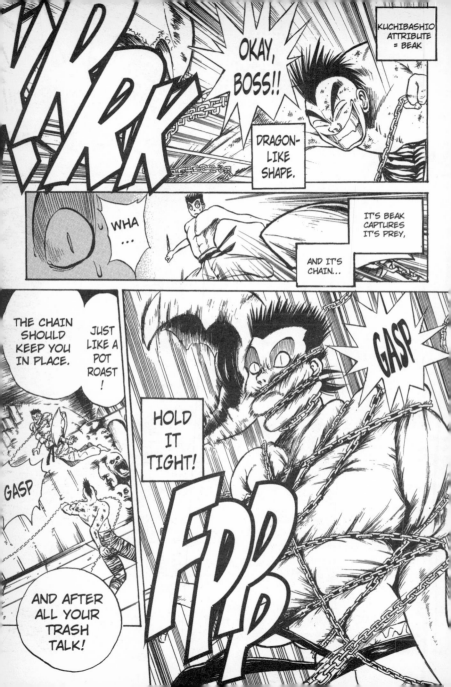

IRON FIST PUNISHMENT !!

HAAK

NEXT TIME, WE'LL TRAIN YOUR BRAIN!!

DUMMY!! IF YOU'D USED YOUR SECRET WEAPON SOONER YOU WOULDN'T HAVE GOTTEN BEATEN UP SO BAD!!

...

FWUMP!!

WA HA HA .... HUH?

I WON !!

CRITIQUE: NEEDS A LOT OF WORK. (FUKO)

OOoo

DOUBLE KNOCK OUT!! DRAW!!

...NEXT BATTLE

FUJIMARU   FUKO

YOU SAID HE'D WIN FOR SURE.

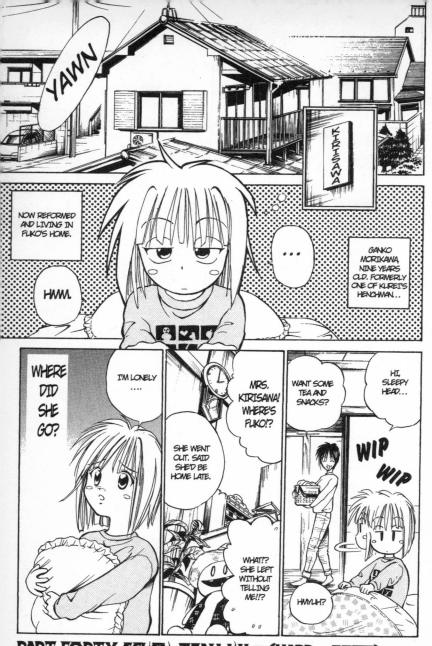

PART FORTY-SEVEN: TEAM KU 3 (HARD + SOFT)

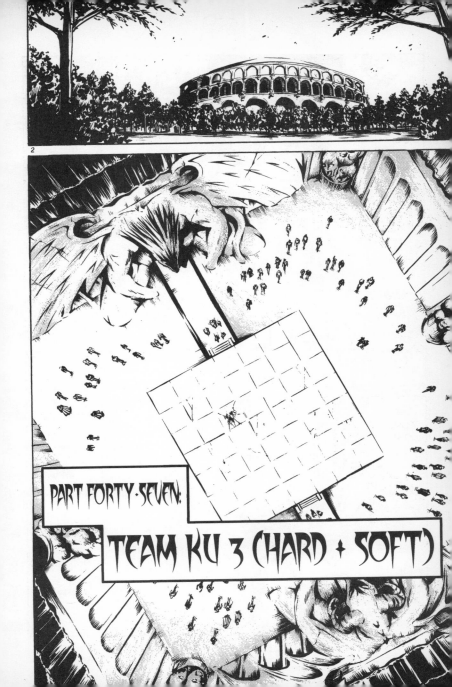

PART FORTY·SEVEN:

TEAM KU 3 (HARD + SOFT')

DAIKOKU ✕-○ MIKAGAMI

NAMIO △-△ DOMON

THE FIRST THREE MEAN NOTHING,

DON'T FOOL YOURSELF.

ONE WIN, ONE DRAW! GOOD START!

BUT IF FUKO CAN WIN THE NEXT MATCH WE'LL BE IN GOOD SHAPE.

IF FUKO LOSES...

BUT I WANT TO FIGHT KUKAI...

I'LL HAVE TO FIGHT BOTH OF THEM.

LET'S NOT GIVE HIM A CHANCE TO SHOW US WHAT HE CAN DO!! FINISH IT WITH THE FOURTH MATCH!

I SENSE SOMETHING EXTRAORDINARY ABOUT KUKAI.

THE TIDE TURNS AGAINST US IF SHE DOESN'T WIN.

BUT SHE HAS TO FACE SAICHO, ONE OF KU'S BEST FIGHTERS.

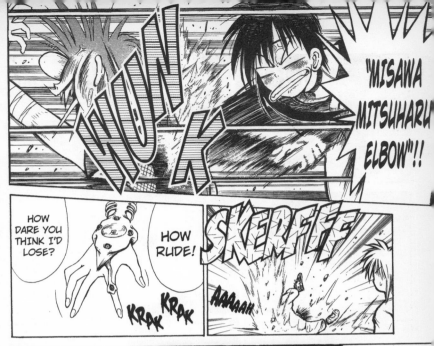

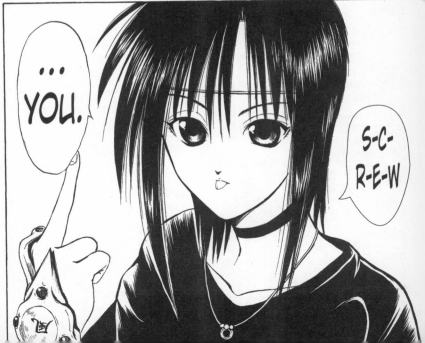

MORE THAN WE CAN IMAGINE...

SHE IS AMAZING.

NOW, NOW...

IT WAS YOUR OWN FAULT.

THAT HURT!!

YOU CALL YOURSELVES THE BEST OF THE NORTHEAST! YOU CAN'T EVEN BEAT A BUNCH OF BABIES!!

WHAT'S THIS!? IS THIS THE BEST KU CAN DO!?

SAICHO, PAPER!

SKRITCH SKRITCH

HO NK

THEY'RE NO ORDINARY KIDS...

I'M SORRY, MASTER KUKAI...

WE HAVE SHAMED THE NAME OF KU...

THOSE BASTARDS! THEY CAN SAY THAT BECAUSE THEY HAVEN'T FOUGHT THEM..

131

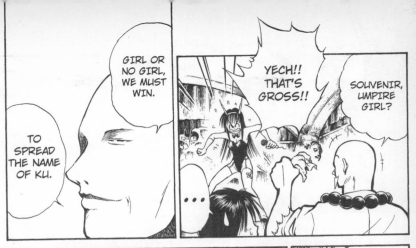

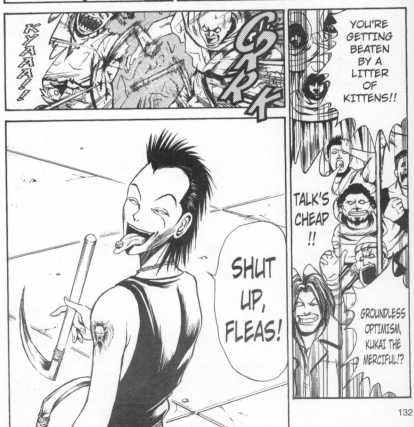

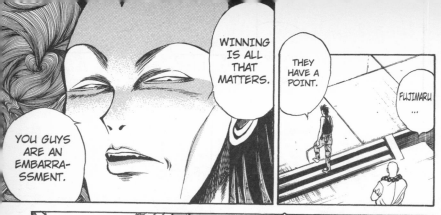

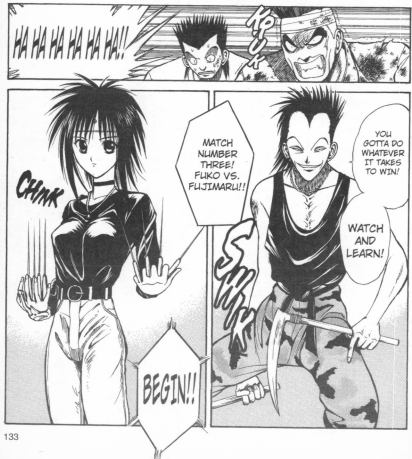

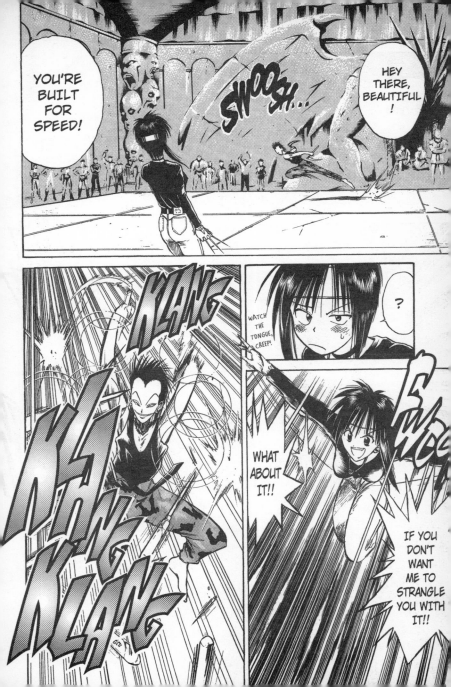

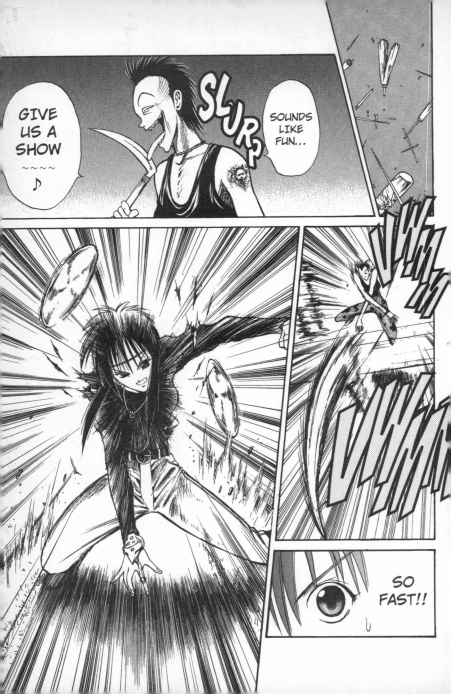

SWAP

GRRROWR ♡ HEE HEE!!

GIVE US A STRIP SHOW ～ ♪

RSSK

OH ...!

GR

RR

I'M IN COMPLETE CONTROL.

FSSSS

I'M PERFECTLY CALM.

EASY, FUKO! DON'T LET HIM GET TO YOU!!

SNAP...

SHURP

HE WANTS YOU TO LOOSE YOUR HEAD!!

136

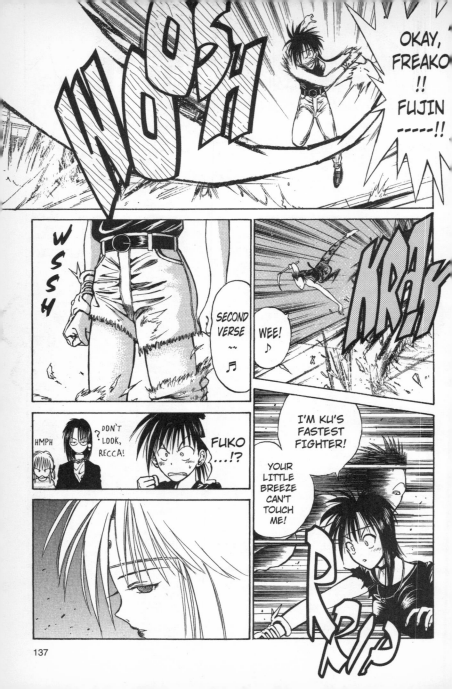

TSUME (CLAW)

IT'S GOTTA BE CLOSE COMBAT.

SKERF

SKERF

• • •

IS THAT TSUME-MARU'S?

THAT'S BOLD OF HER.

SHE'S GOING TO USE THAT?

THAT'S... THE *CLAW* SPHERE!?

SWUD

YES... IT IS.

FUJIN PLUS...

THE DEVIL'S CLAW...

138

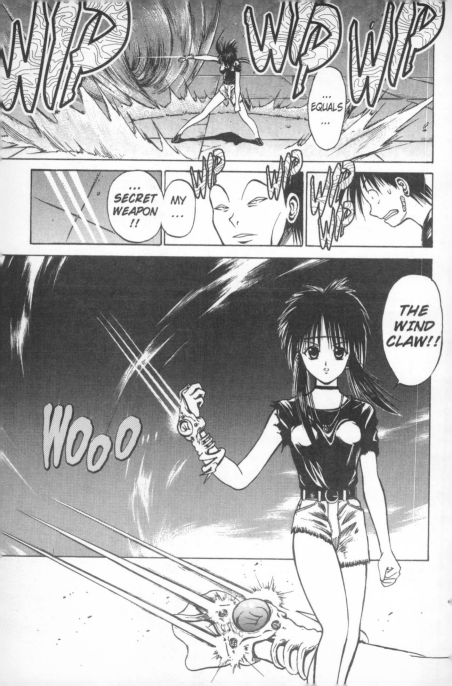

I'VE NEVER SEEN THIS DONE BEFORE.

SHE'S COMBINED TWO MADOGUS...

WHAT'S GOING ON!?

FUJIN AND THE DEVIL'S CLAW MERGED!?

IS MISSING ITS SPHERE? THE WIND SPHERE!

KAGERŌ, WHY IS IT THAT MY FUJIN...

FUKO SPOKE TO ME BEFORE SHE LEFT FOR TRAINING...

I PUT IT IN TO CONFUSE YOU. FORGIVE ME.

THAT WAS A FAKE.

REALLY! BUT DIDN'T IT HAVE A SPHERE WHEN YOU FIRST GAVE IT TO ME?

FUJIN IS ONE OF THE DEADLIEST OF ALL MADOGUS! THE FOUR SMALL SPHERES CAN CREATE WIND EVEN WITHOUT THE CORE SPHERE.

風

KAZE (WIND)

THE WHEREABOUTS OF THE CORE SPHERE IS UNKNOWN. THIS TALISMAN IS NOT FULLY ENABLED. WITH ITS CORE SPHERE IT WOULD BE UNSTOPPABLE!

HMM...

SO...

I COULD PUT A DIFFERENT SPHERE IN HERE, COULDN'T I?

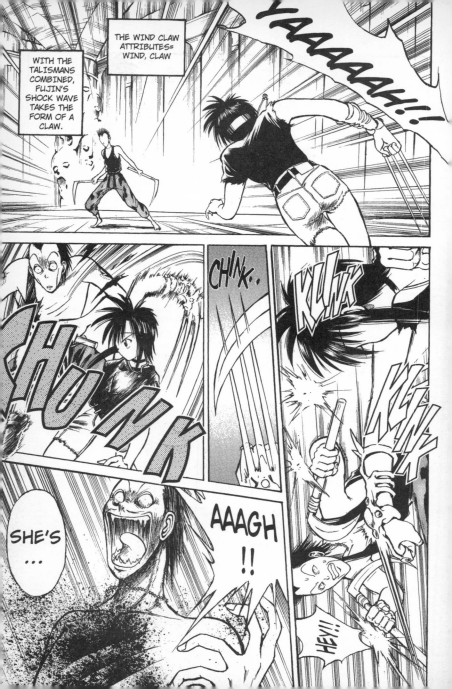

VERY CLEVER.

AND HER SOFTWARE IS DRIVING HER HARDWARE IN UNDREAMED OF WAYS!

THE SOFTWARE DRIVES HARDWARE, BRAIN DRIVES TALISMANS...

AS IN YOUR VIDEO GAMES...

FUKO, CLEVER!?

SHE'S INNOVATIVE, A BRILLIANT MADOGU WIELDER!!

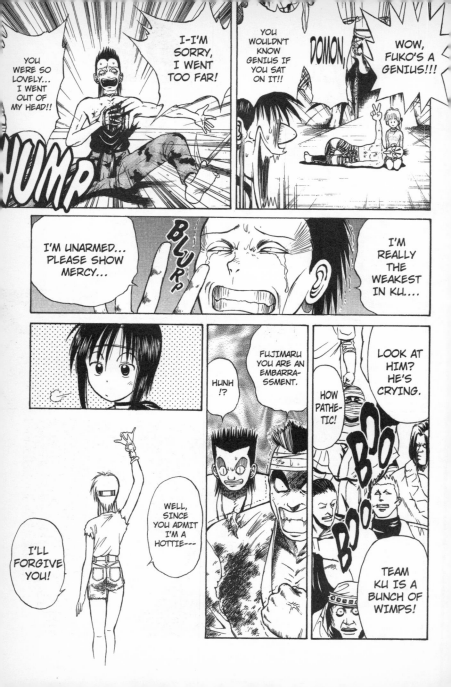

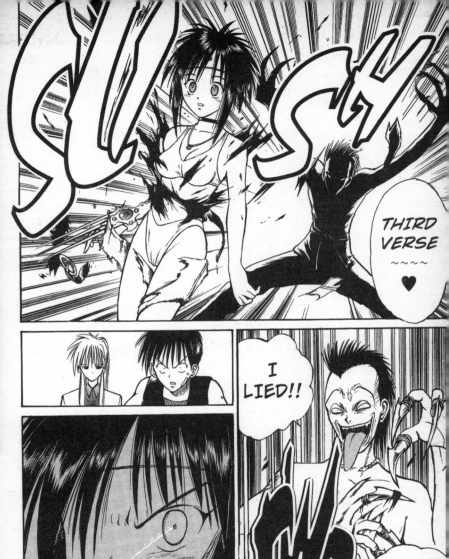

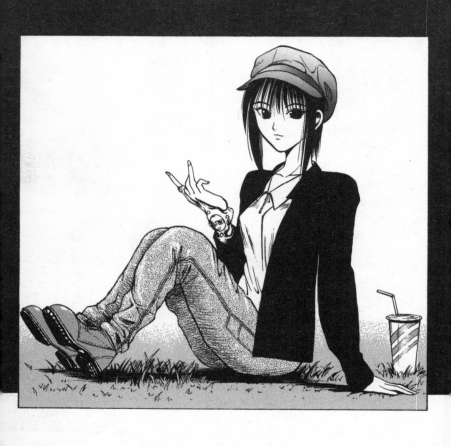

PART FORTY-EIGHT:

KU 4 (HURRICANE FUKO)

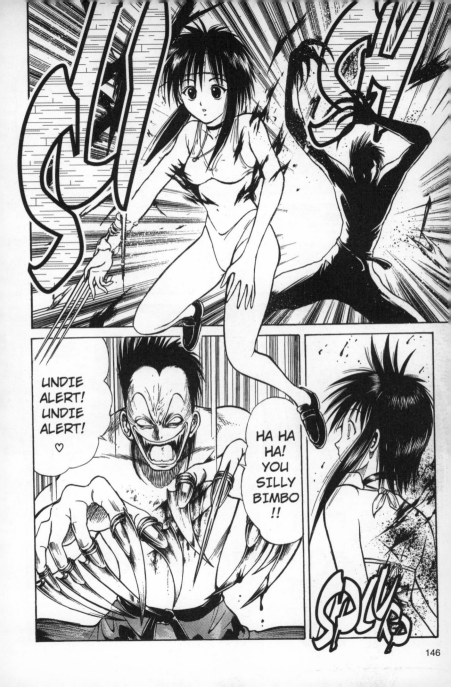

146

YOU'RE AS STUPID AS YOU ARE UGLY!!

ONLY AN AMATEUR-- AND A FOOL-- WOULD TURN HER BACK ON AN ENEMY!

WHY THAT DIRTY FREAK!!

FUKO!!

...

YOU...

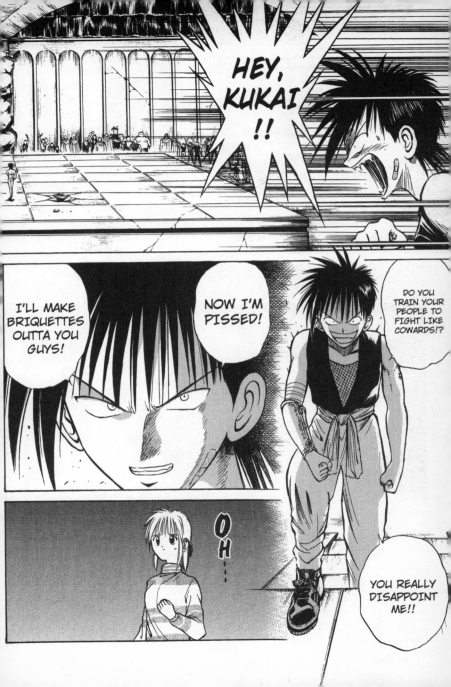

FUJIMARU'S SHAMING ALL OF US! WE SHOULD NEVER HAVE ALLOWED HIM TO FIGHT!

MASTER KUKAI!! WILL YOU LET HIM GET AWAY WITH THAT!?

PLEASE TAKE HIM OUT, MASTER!!

MASTER KUKAI...

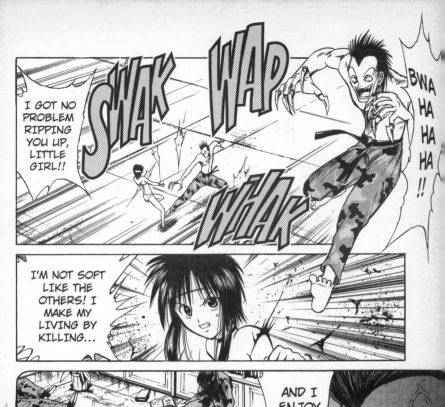

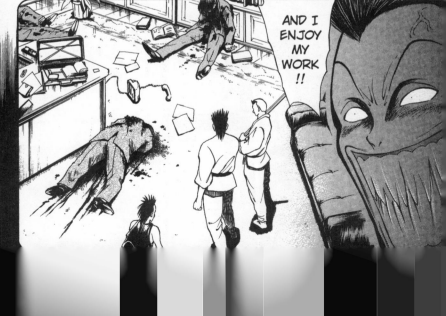

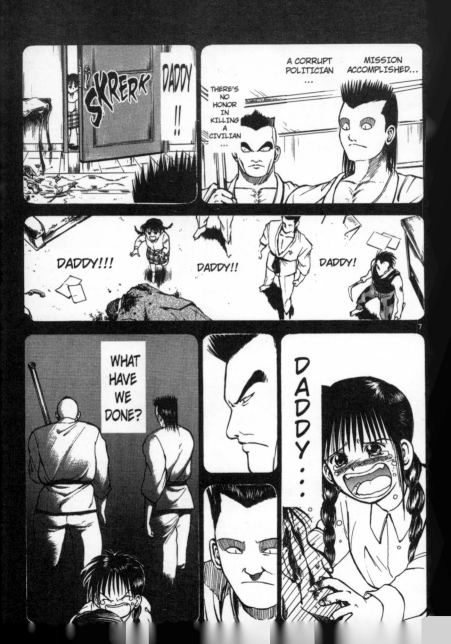

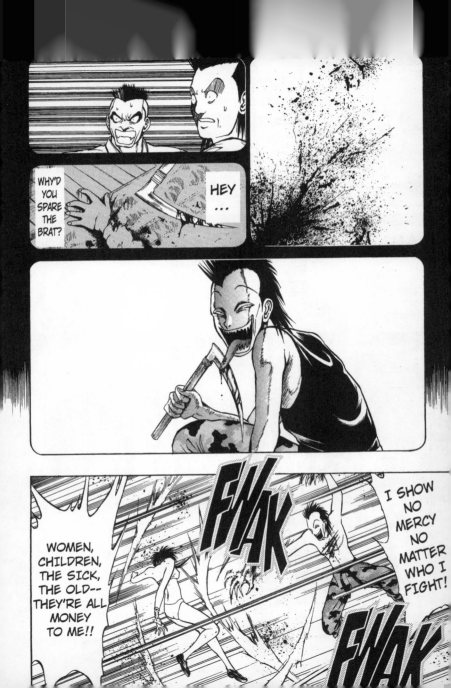

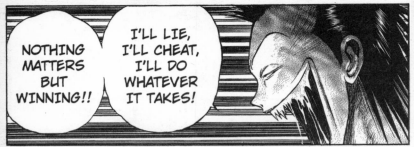

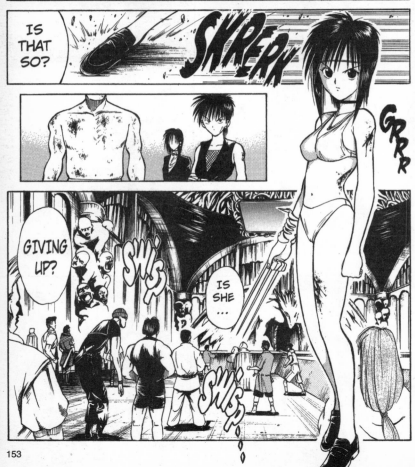

153

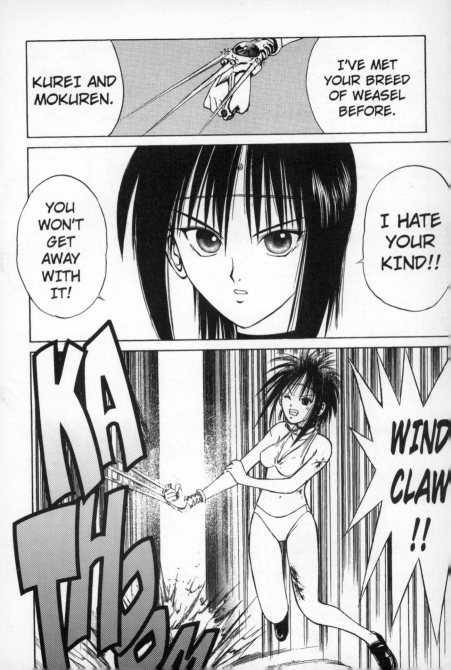

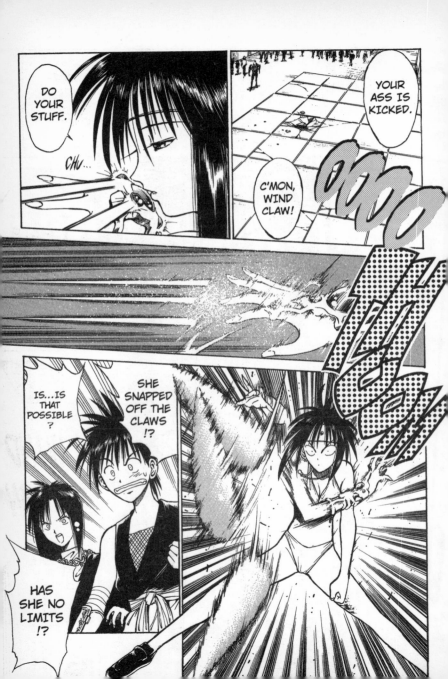

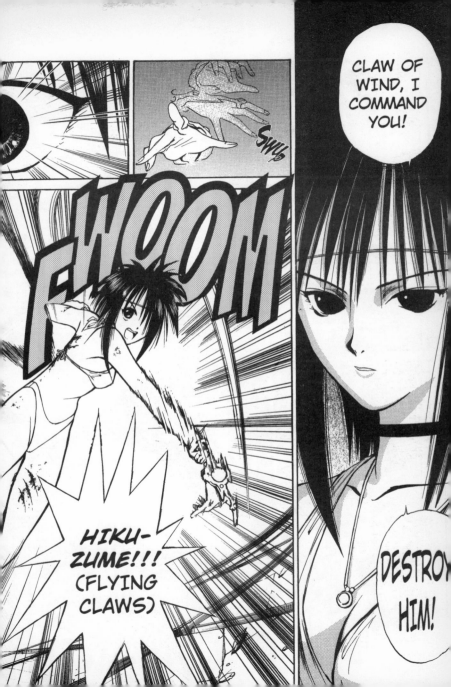

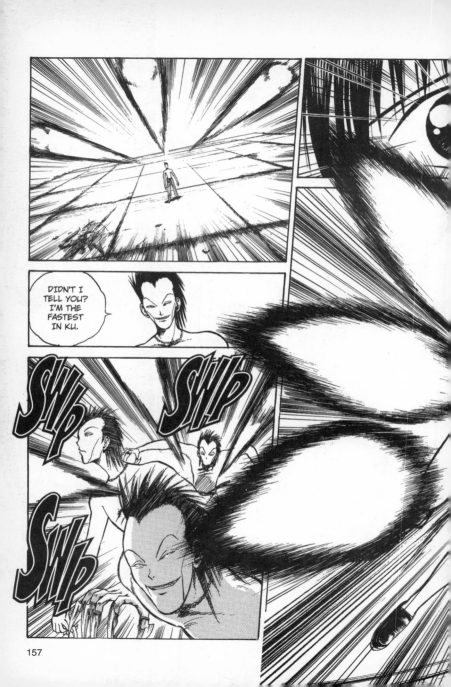

HE'S SLIPPERY!!

HE DODGED CLAWS!!

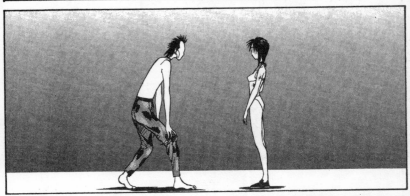

I'M SORRY. ♡

IT'S ALL OVER NOW, CHICKIE!

HUFF

DARN.

HUFF

HUFF

HUFF

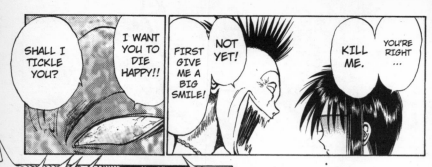

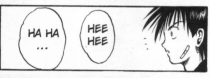

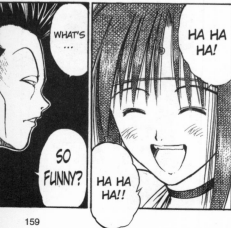

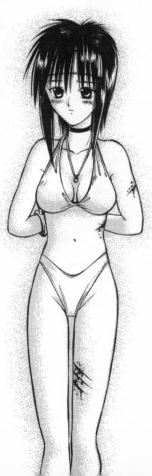

159

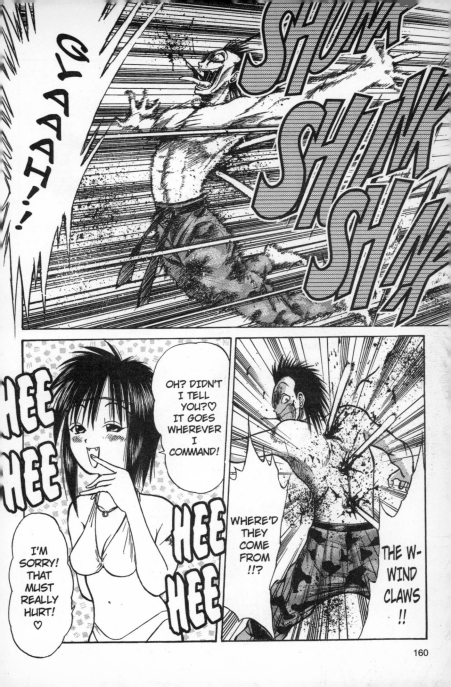

160

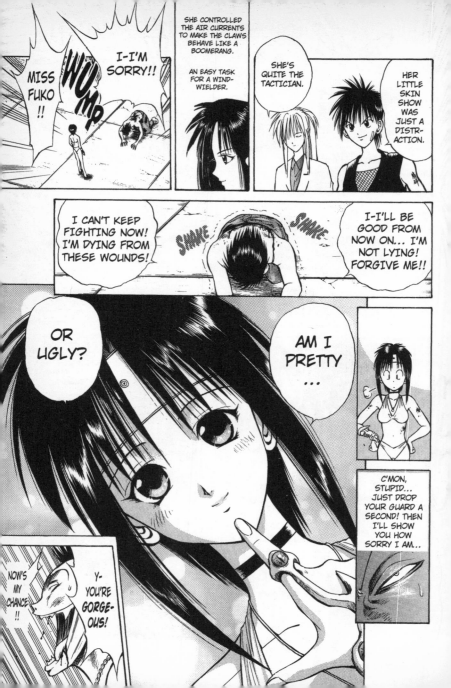

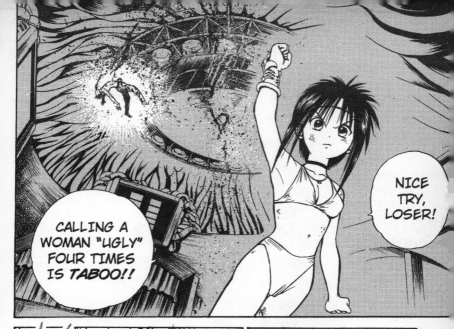

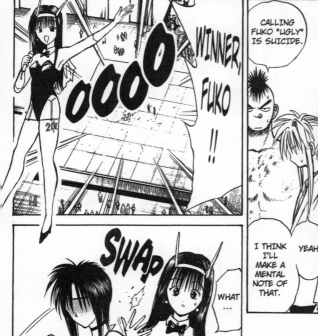

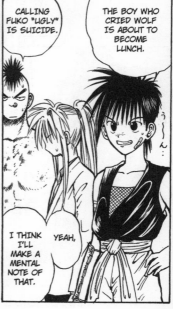

162

IF THERE'S MORE OF YOU LIKE HIM, WATCH OUT!!

LISTEN UP, YOU SCUMBAGS!!

I'LL KICK ALL YOUR BUTTS!!

FUKO'S HERE AND SHE'S NOT TAKING DISRESPECT!

BELIEVE ME,

I APOLOGIZE FOR FUJIMARU.

TEAM KU DOES NOT CONDONE NEEDLESS KILLING.

TMP

WHAT A TOUGH CHICK!

WUSP

WUSP

DROP THE ATTITUDE.

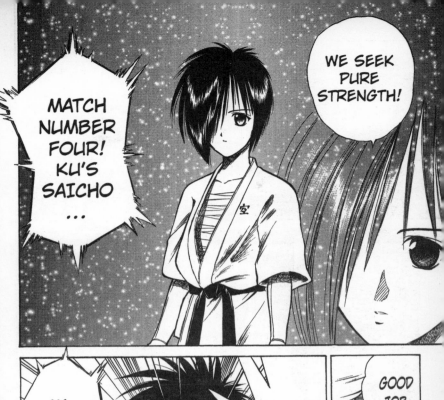

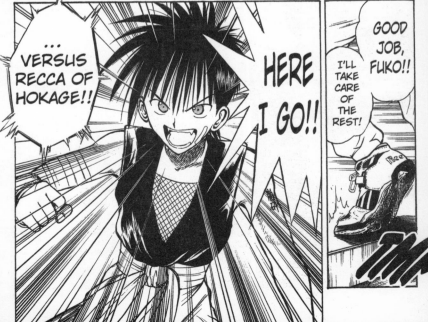

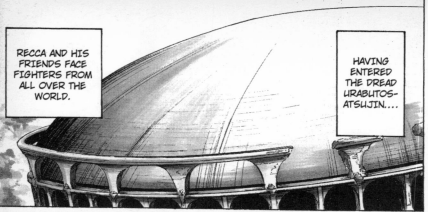

RECCA AND HIS FRIENDS FACE FIGHTERS FROM ALL OVER THE WORLD.

HAVING ENTERED THE DREAD URABUTOS-ATSUJIN....

THE NORTHEAST'S TOP DEATH SQUAD...

IN THEIR FIRST FIGHT THEY FACE TEAM KU...

WITH THE GAME ON THE LINE, A YOUNG MAN STEPS INTO THE RING.

THE BEST 3 OUT OF 5 MATCHES WINS. RECCA'S TEAM CURRENTLY HAS 2 WINS AND A DRAW.

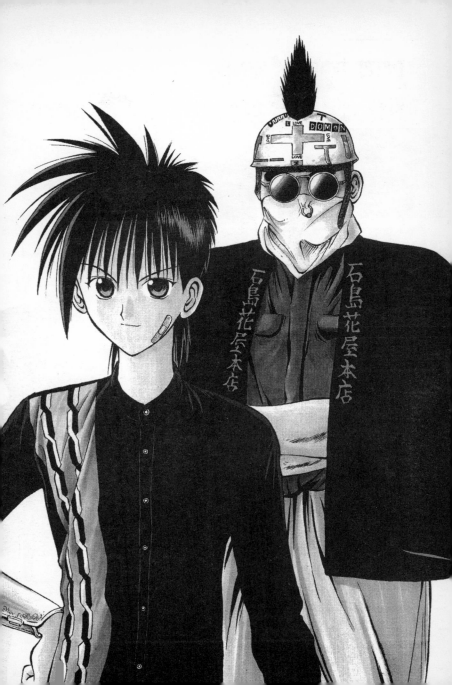

PART FORTY-NINE:
KU 5 (A BLIZZARD OF PAPER)

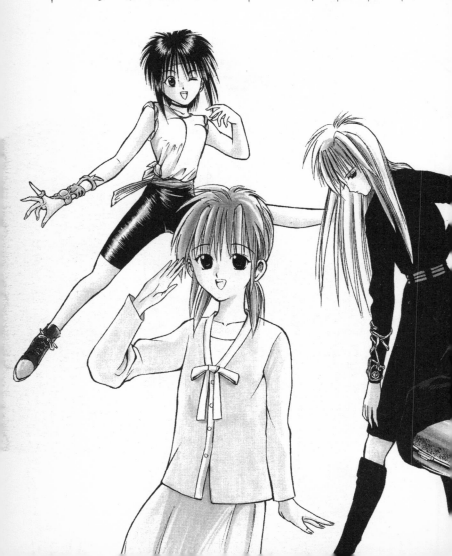

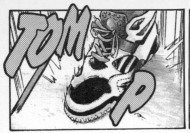

RECCA OF HOKAGE!!

MATCH NUMBER FOUR!!

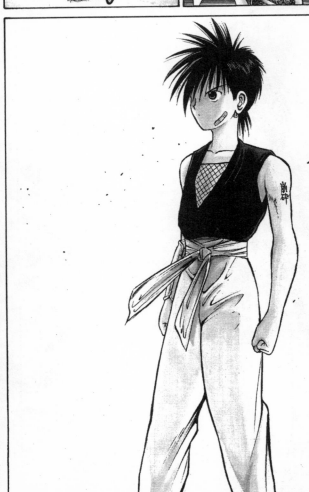

TEAM KU, WITH ITS BACK AGAINST THE WALL NOW, IS REPRESENTED BY SAICHO!!!

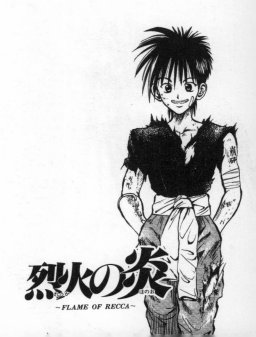

烈火の炎
~FLAME OF RECCA~

SAICHO!
SAICHO!
SAICHO!

SAICHO IS RANKED SECOND IN TEAM KU!!

KNOCK HIS HEAD IN!!

OOOO

SPANK THOSE BABIES, KU!

HOKAGE SUCKS! YOU GUYS LOOK LIKE SISSIES !!

KILL! KILL!!

AND... DAINTY!

HE LOOKS SO YOUNG, THOUGH.

REMEMBER, SAICHO...

FIFTEEN MINUTES!

FINISH HIM WITHIN IN THAT TIME.

AND AFTER THAT I'LL SLAUGHTER 'EM LIKE PUPPIES!

GOOD! WE'LL BE TIED IF BOTH YOU AND MASTER KU WIN!!

I KNOW.

I'LL TAKE HIM OUT FAST.

OR ELSE ...YOU KNOW.

TMP

172

!?

SAICHO IS
FIGHTING TO
REMOVE THE
STAIN YOU
PUT ON KU'S
HONOR.

SHUT UP,
FUJIMARU
...

173

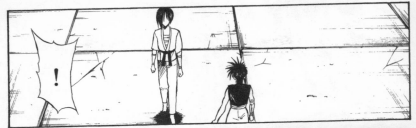

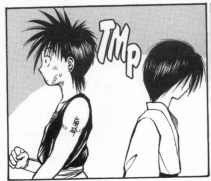

WHAT'S HE GONNA DO!?

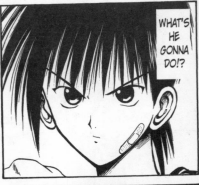

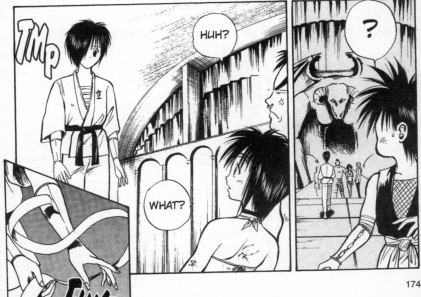

HUH?

WHAT?

?

174

PLEASE PARDON KU FOR FUJIMARU'S BEHAVIOR.

ULP

...

NOT ALL OF US ARE LIKE FUJIMARU.

I HOPE YOU WILL BELIEVE ...

SWUP

THIS BANDAGE,

IT'S... PAPER.

HEY?

QUIET!

HE'S A GENTLE MAN.

HA! SHOWOFF.

SWAP

LET THE 4TH MATCH BEGIN!!

I'LL PROVE IT TO YOU IN BATTLE.

BUT FIRST...

SMILE

FUJIMARU'S PROBABLY JUST YOUR BLACK SHEEP.

YOU'RE ALL RIGHT.

SWUp...

KRK

FWIK...

FWAP

FWAP FWAP

AWAY LITTLE WAGTAIL ...

IS FLYING !!?

THAT PAPER CRANE ...

THAT'S MY TALENT.

WOW !

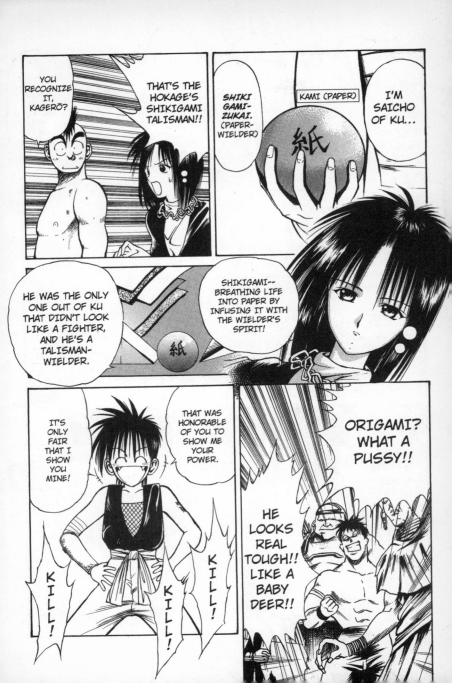

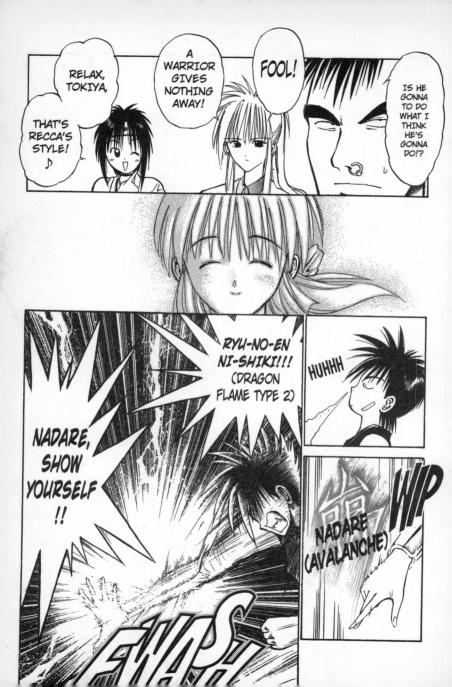

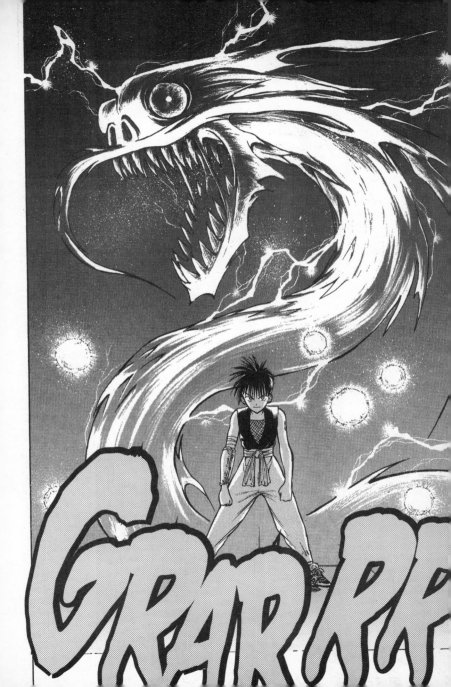

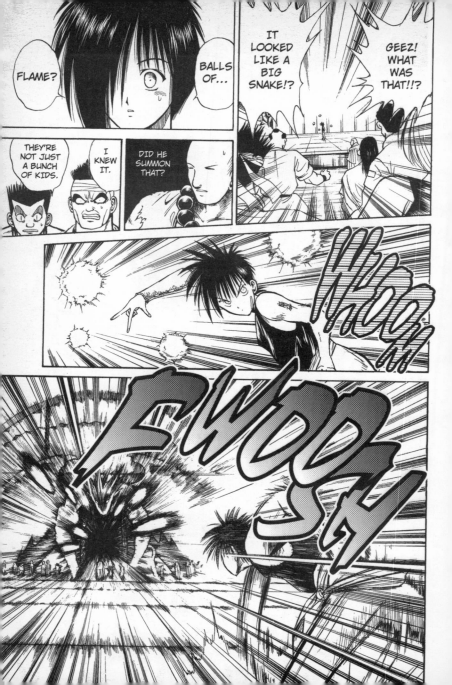

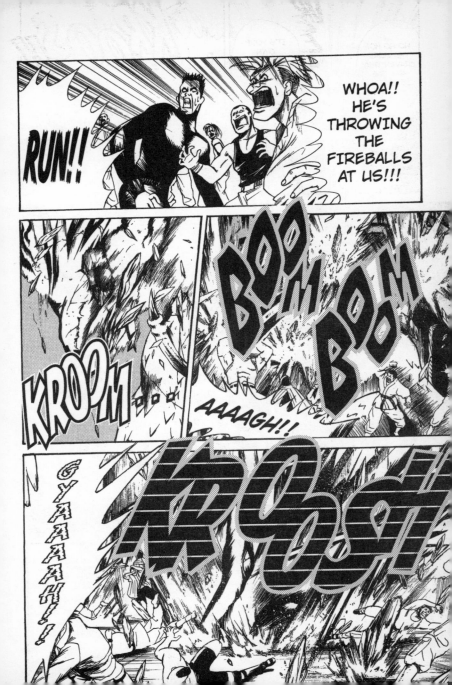

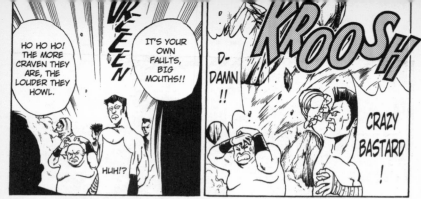

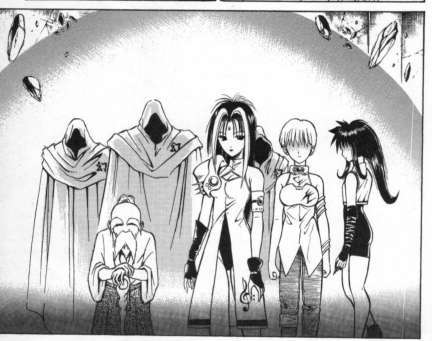

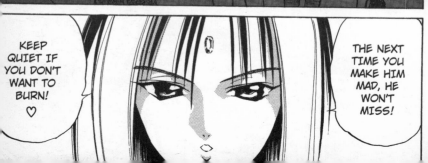

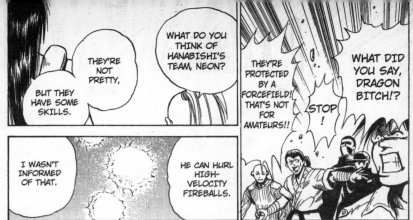

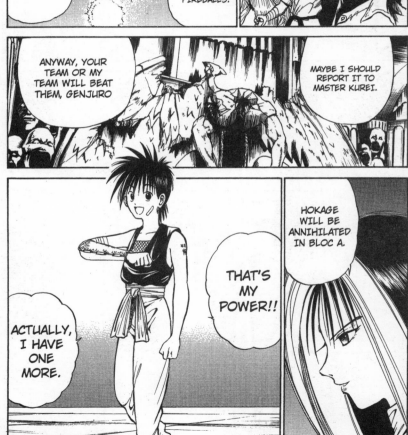

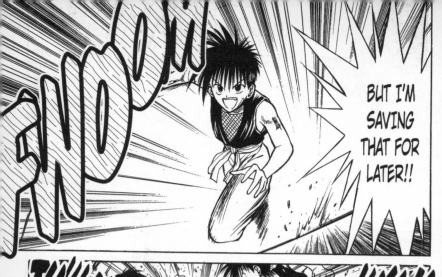

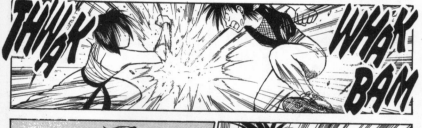

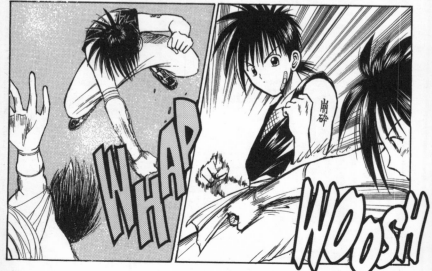

185

HUH
...

SAICHO, REMEMBER! FIFTEEN MINUTES!

USE THE SHIKI-GAMI!!

SAICHO IS AT A DISADVANTAGE IN CLOSE COMBAT.

RECCA FIGHTS LIKE A SEASONED VETERAN.

OKAY!

LOOK OUT, RECCA!!

HE'S UP TO SOMETHING!!

THE PAPER BANDAGE!!

WOOOOOOO

"THE JEALOUSY OF THE THREE TRANSMIGRATING SOULS, I WORSHIP THE PRINCESS OF UJI BRIDGE ..."

KAMIENBU!!! (PAPER STAGE SHOW)

HERE IT COMES, RECCA!!!!

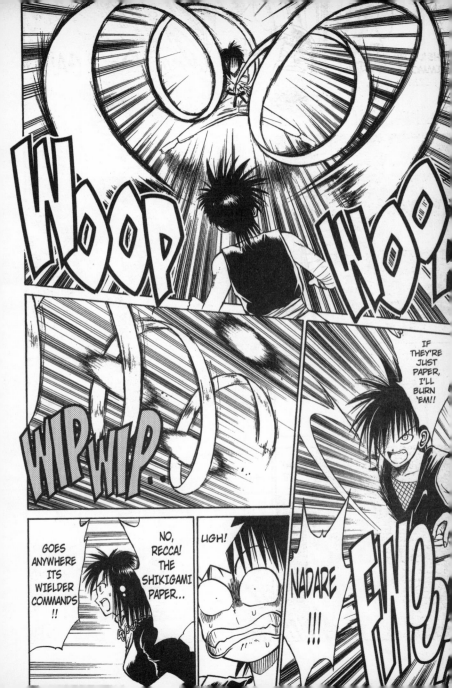

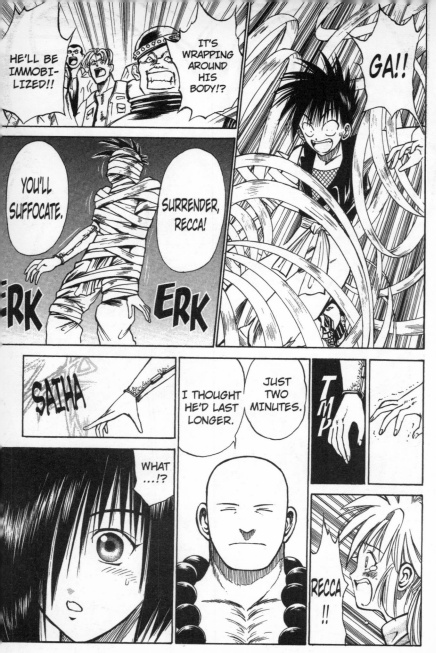

189

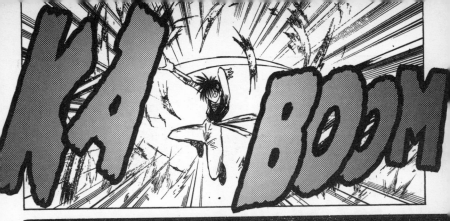

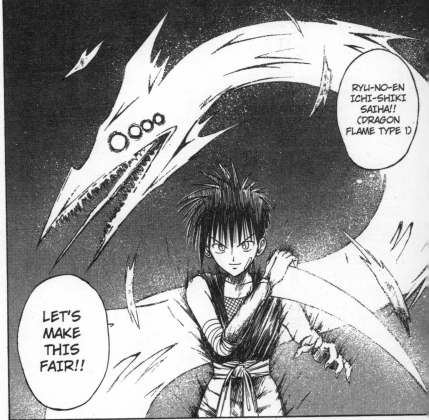

TO BE CONTINUED!!!

MY PICTURE DIARY

KUROGANE (IRON) KOBUSHI

TEKKEN VERSION

NOT
FUKO

I AM TRULY GRATEFUL. REALLY!

I'M ALWAYS DELIGHTED THAT SO MANY PEOPLE OUT THERE WANT TO READ MY MANGA.

THE MOST INTENSE OF THEM ALL.

SO I THOUGHT I'D PRESENT A COUPLE THAT I THOUGHT WERE

SM NAWATCH BRINGS THEM TO ME.

I'M SURPRISED BY YOUR CUTTING CRITICISM. IT'S NOT RARE THAT IT MAKES ITS WAY INTO THE MANGA!

I LOVE FAN LETTERS BECAUSE IT'S MY ONLY WAY OF COMMUNICATING WITH MY READERS!! (I KNOW IT'S ONE-SIDED.)

I PUT UP THE DRAWINGS I LIKE IN FRONT OF MY DESK SO I REMEMBER THAT WAY, TOO.

I HAVE A GOOD MEMORY EVEN THOUGH I'M NOT THE BRIGHTEST GUY. AFTER THREE OR FIVE LETTERS, I'LL REMEMBER THEIR NAMES.

DRAWINGS, STICKERS, KEY-HOLDERS, MANGAS, TAPES, CALENDARS, AND UM... UM...

Yuimu Rei (Tokyo)

Ho Hoshikage ho ho Kira ho (Shimane)

I THOUGHT I'D INTRODUCE A FEW I THINK ARE ESPECIALLY INTENSE.

I DON'T CHASE AFTER THOSE WHO ~~VE!~~

SOME WROTE A LOT BEFORE, THEN ABRUPTLY STOPPED WRITING.

LEAVES QUITE AN IMPRES-SION WHEN YOU SEND THOSE KINDS OF THINGS IN.

...LYS REALLY DO SO MUCH. REPEAT CUSTOMERS!
...G FOR THE TITLE OF "QUEEN."

COS-PURE (COSTUME PLAY/DRESSING UP)

RECCA'S DAD

SENT ME A LETTER.

THE LETTER READ: "PLEASE RECOGNIZE COS-PURE." IF YOU LIKE MY MANGA THAT MUCH, GO KNOCK YOURSELVES OUT.

WOW, THERE ARE PEOPLE WHO DO THESE KINDS OF THINGS.

I'M GRATE-FUL.

A REAL MOHAWK!! HE'S NOT PLAYING.

DOMON'S THE CRAZIEST

WRITING DAD ON APRON, HOW COOL!

TOBI-RECCA HANDSOME

RECCA'S DAD

NOT TOO MANY OF MIKAGAMI AND KOGANEI. (SOME FROM THE HARDCORE FANS.)

------AND....

MOST OF THE DRAWINGS ARE OF RECCA, FUKO, AND YANAGI. (SURPRISINGLY A LOT OF YOEN AND KUREI.)

HOW WILL ANYBODY KNOW YOU'RE MIKAGA-MI?

EVEN GIRLS SENT IN LETTERS SAYING, "CHECK OUT MY MIKAGAMI COS-PURE! I DON'T HAVE ENSUI BUT."

I'M THINKING ABOUT SHOWING SOME OF THE DRAWINGS IN HERE.

(IS HE HATED?)

HARDLY ANY.

SEE YOU NEXT TIME.